'What did y
demanded ra

'Shock tactics?'

'Then I suggest y   keep your tactics to yourself.' But her words were weak, unmeant. Kenda wanted him back in her arms.

'Don't like a taste of your own medicine?'

'You don't know what my medicine is like.'

'No, but I've guessed,' he said quietly. 'Constantly.'

'What?'

'More?' Carrick Lorne-Howell the Third taunted.

'No,' she said, meaning yes. 'And I suggest you find another deterrent.'

'But I like this one.' Gathering her against him, he kissed her again.

Emma Richmond was born during the war in north Kent when, she says, 'Farms were the norm and motorways non-existent. My childhood was one of warmth and adventure. Amiable and disorganized, I'm married with three daughters, all of whom have fled the nest—probably out of exasperation! The dog stayed, reluctantly. I'm an avid reader, a compulsive writer and a besotted new granny. I love life and my world of dreams, and all I need to make things complete is a housekeeper—like, yesterday!'

Recent titles by the same author:

THE BACHELOR CHASE
HAVING IT ALL!
FIRST-TIME FATHER

BEHAVING BADLY!

BY
EMMA RICHMOND

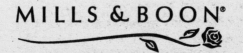

*First published in Great Britain 1997
Harlequin Mills & Boon Limited,
Eton House, 18-24 Paradise Road, Richmond, Surrey TW9 1SR*

© Emma Richmond 1997

ISBN 0 263 80036 9

*Set in Times Roman 11 on 12 pt.
02-9703-48788 C1*

*Printed and bound in Great Britain
by Mackays of Chatham PLC, Chatham*

CHAPTER ONE

'Is it a game?' a neutral voice asked from behind her.

'Yes,' Kenda said savagely. 'It's called Hell Hath No Fury!'

'Who did the scorning?'

'Mind your own business!' Tall, statuesque, her tawny hair tangled from her exertions, topaz eyes filled with bitter fury, she frustratedly abandoned her futile attempt to break a golf club in half and turned to face the man in the doorway. Mouth open to continue her remonstration, she just—stared, felt a swift flare of astonished attraction. *Such is the stuff of dreams,* she thought stupidly. Tall, fit, brown hair damp and windswept, penetrating grey eyes. Arrogant, sexy—devastating.

He gave a mocking lift of his eyebrows, and she flushed, all fancies instantly dismissed. 'Who the hell are you?'

Distastefully pedantic, he drawled, 'Carrick Lorne-Howell the Third.'

'Carrick L...' Unbelievably shocked, she just stared at him. *This* was the man she was to be employed by? The man whose castle she was to present herself at on the following day? The man who was grudgingly allowing her to work for him? She'd expected—well, she didn't know what she'd expected—a crusty old fanatic, she supposed, because, from all she'd heard, he was fanatical about the ancient weapons that he collected and

5

taught people to use. Which had led her to suppose
that he'd be *old*, and he wasn't. He couldn't be
more than thirty-five.

Mesmerised, mentally off balance because he'd
come as such a shock, barely aware of what she
said, she demanded rudely, 'And what are you
doing *here*? Checking out the staff? Or hoping I
might miraculously have turned into a male?'

'You don't become staff until Monday—and I've
never yet witnessed a miracle.' Moving his eyes away
from her—the cold grey eyes of a man who thought
a lot and said little—he stared at the shredded suit,
the ripped shirts and ties, the stabbed shoes, the
torn paper that lay like confetti across the wide
double bed, and gave a thin smile.

'Bad taste in men?'

'No. How do you break golf clubs?'

'You don't.'

With a dismissive shrug—or a shrug she hoped
looked dismissive, because she was still off balance
from the sheer impact of him—she walked across
to the window, opened it, hurled out the club she
still held, and then picked up the bag standing
beside her and emptied the contents into the flower-
bed below. 'I might be at the castle early,' she stated
tightly.

'Or dead.'

'Or dead,' she agreed flatly, because, quite
possibly, Richard *might* kill her when he discovered what she had done to his possessions. 'In
which case,' she continued, 'you'd have to find
another historian, because if I have *my* way Richard
"Cheating" Marsh won't be coming to your castle
either!'

'Tiresome,' he agreed, 'but not an insur-mountable problem.'

'No.' Glaring at the golf bag she still held, she flung it away with a gesture of distaste. 'How did you know who I was?'

'You were—described to me.'

'Who by?'

'Does it matter?'

'No,' she retorted crossly, 'but I can guess the content. Man-eater? Man-hater?' she queried pithily. He merely smiled. Aggravatingly. 'And if you were looking for Richard he's out checking golf courses.'

He glanced at the discarded golf bag, returned his eyes to hers. 'I wasn't. I came to meet someone.'

'In this room?' she asked haughtily.

'No, his.'

'Then hadn't you better go and *meet* him?'

He gave a small nod and walked away. Bastard. Cold, unfeeling, arrogant bastard. Hard and fit. Complete. Indifferent to other people's pain. She wished *she* were—wished she were indifferent to *everything*! And what malicious god had decreed that he should walk past at this precise moment?

Unemployable for months, she'd now probably alienated the one man who was prepared to employ her. Reluctantly, she assumed, seeing as he'd wanted a male historian—and someone with an unblem-ished record, she thought with a bitter smile. At least he hadn't told her not to come. A small comfort.

With an angry twitch, so very strong-willed, she dismissed him from her mind. Attractive men were ten a penny; it was the *nature* that counted. And his nature looked—scathing. Richard's nature, on the other hand, was despicable.

Angry and hurt, her need for revenge in no way abated, she turned to survey her handiwork, and gave a grim smile of satisfaction. Let him explain *that* to the hotel staff! Lying, dishonourable *rat*!

Kicking aside one of his brown shoes, which still sported the scissors, she stalked across to her own room and repacked what she had so very recently unpacked. And if he thought that that was the end of it he had another think coming. Oh, *boy*, did he have another think coming! Grabbing her coat, bag and suitcase, she walked down to Reception.

Giving the girl a brittle smile, she informed her, 'Room 309 is now vacant. Mr Marsh will pay anything that's owing. Goodbye.'

Without waiting for an answer, she marched out, briefly surveyed the puddles in the car park, stared at the lowering sky, the rain that was beginning *again*, and stalked across to her car. She flung her case into the boot, climbed behind the wheel and drove off.

Fool, she castigated herself. Don't you *ever* learn? Teeth gritted, eyes smarting, she hastily pulled off the road and turned off the engine. How *could* he? She'd thought him her *friend*! He'd always been so nice, seemed so genuine. So encouraging! And as for Carrick! How *dared* he judge her? Because he *had* judged, just like everyone did. Those cold grey eyes had held distaste. *And* mockery. So let him mock; she didn't care that he probably thought she and Richard were lovers, that they'd had a tiff. Lover? She hadn't had a lover for *years*!

Sniffing, scrubbing angrily at her eyes, she stared bleakly through the windscreen. She wouldn't mind Carrick for a lover... Oh, shut up!

With her striking, memorable face Kenda was a very vibrant person. Quick to anger, quick to forgive. Generous, impulsive, headstrong. And a fool, she thought bleakly. At least where men were concerned.

How could she always be so disastrously wrong about them? And what was she supposed to do now? Carry on as though nothing had happened? There wasn't anything else *to* do! She couldn't go home, because she didn't have one! Couldn't afford to rent because she didn't have any money, which was why she'd jumped at the chance to come down here.

Oh, to hell with it, she thought bitterly; she'd go to the castle. If she didn't, Carrick Lorne-Howell looked the sort of man to sue her for breach of contract or something.

Shoving everything from her mind, fighting anger and pain, she switched on the engine, glared through the rain-spattered windscreen at dripping hedgerows, soggy sheep that wandered all over the road, and gave a long sigh. She *hated* the country!

Hurt, angry and bewildered, she tried to dismiss the last few hours from her mind, and couldn't. All she could think about was Richard Marsh. Everything else was peripheral. And if he *dared* show his face at the castle...

Not that it was really a castle, she discovered— more a manor house with turrets, and not even old. Not even *found* if she hadn't been given a detailed map. Halting at the end of the tree-lined track, she stared at it. Pretentious, she decided, and desperation meant that she would be stuck in it for weeks! Weeks of scenery, she thought despondently. Woodland, fields, little streams that meandered. Lorna Doone country. Sometimes bleak, always beautiful—if you liked that sort of thing.

Kenda didn't. She liked cities. The bigger the better. But, circumstances being what they were— no money, no job—Carrick's offer had been one she'd been unable to refuse. Offer? she scoffed. It had been reluctant agreement. Be nice to him, Richard had said. He's very influential. Huh.

Staring at the castle—the castle that had been built by Carrick's great-great-grandfather for his wife because she had yearned for one, or so Richard had told her, she wondered rather bleakly what it would be like to be loved that much. Pretty special, she imagined, and something, the way things were going, that she was never likely to find out for herself. Anyway, they probably didn't make men like that any more. Or if they did she'd never met one.

Certainly the man she was about to be employed by didn't look like that. He looked—distant, pedantic, self-contained. Arrogant. And if he'd met up with Richard—which was extremely likely because he looked the sort of man to stick his nose into other people's affairs—found out why she'd shredded his possessions, then he would take Richard 'Cheating' Marsh's side against her own. *That* went without saying. Men *always* stuck together. In fact, Richard was probably, at this very minute, justifying himself to Carrick.

Her mood growing savage again, she put the car in gear, drove the last few yards crossed cautiously over the drawbridge and into the exercise yard. There was no outer ward, no moat, just the arch that led to the inner courtyard and the great hall.

It was still drizzling with rain. Parking in the far corner, she climbed out, collected her luggage and, stepping carefully on the rain-slick cobbles, went to tug on the ancient bell pull.

An old man opened the door. Eventually. When her hair had become thoroughly soaked. The family retainer, no doubt, she thought sourly. Carrick Lorne-Howell looked the sort to want one.

'You should have a porch,' she grumbled crossly. 'Kenda McKinley. I'm early,' she added baldly. 'Is it a problem?'

He looked momentarily startled, then shook his head. 'No,' he said carefully, 'it isn't a problem. Won't you come in? Dreadful day.'

'Yes.' Utterly, horribly, perfectly dreadful. And not because of the weather.

'Carrick isn't here, I'm afraid,' he explained as he relieved her of her case and led the way across the echoing hall.

'No, I know. I've just seen him.' Weapons, shields, armour lined the stone walls; a fire flickered fitfully in the enormous hearth.

'That sounded pithy,' he remarked smoothly.

'It was meant to. This place is freezing! It's a wonder you haven't gone down with pneumonia.'

'Just recovered,' he murmured blandly.

Surprised, because he hadn't actually looked as though he had a sense of humour, she felt her lips twitch. 'Sorry,' she apologised. 'I'm in a foul mood.'

'So I gathered.' Opening a heavy door at the far end of the hall, he held it for her, then followed her through before taking the lead once more. In the narrow passage, on uneven flagstones, she stepped carefully, not wanting to rick her ankle in her high-heeled boots.

For convenience rather than historical accuracy, the kitchen was housed inside the castle instead of outside. Carrick's ancestor might have been eccentric but he hadn't been a fool. Neither was Carrick—the kitchen boasted some of the most modern equipment to be found.

'As you see, the staff quarters are quite pneumonia-proof,' he drawled blandly. He had to look up. In her heeled boots, she topped him by a good three inches. 'Won't you sit down? I feel— dwarfed,' he added wryly. 'I'm Martin, by the way.'

'Mr Martin or Martin something?' she queried as she obediently took a seat at the long oak table. 'And I can't help my height.'

'It wasn't a reproof,' he said humorously. 'And it's Martin something.'

'Hello, Martin something.' Staring round her, she murmured without thinking, 'He must be making money from his weapons training.'

'So I believe. Better than losing it, don't you think?' Setting her case down by the door, he handed her a towel to dry her long hair. 'I'll take your case up presently. Tea? Lunch? There's some lasagne which only needs heating up.'

'Fine. Thank you.'

A twinkle in his dark eyes, he asked, 'Who caused the foulness? Carrick?'

'No. Richard "Cheating" Marsh!'

'Who is?'

'Currently replacing his wardrobe,' Carrick put in smoothly from behind her. 'Not dead, then, I see.'

'Observant,' she muttered rudely.

'Tea? Lasagne?' Martin offered him hastily with a very suspect twitch to his lips.

'Please.' Taking the chair opposite Kenda, Carrick put his elbows on the table, steepled his fingers before his chin, and stared at her. Kenda stared back.

'You got the list?' he asked.

'Yes. Next week the fourteenth century. Two bowmen—Welsh marches, four knights and a couple of foot soldiers.'

'Which means, including ourselves, ten in all.'

'I *can* count. The following week, Romans. And I don't wish to discuss what happened earlier.'

'I wasn't intending to discuss it.'

'Good. Did you manage to get the Imperial Gallic helmets I requested?'

'Yes, I had two made. To your spec. I hope it was correct.'

'It was. You teach them to use the weapons and I'll show them how to dress, how they lived and what they ate.'

He nodded, thanked Martin when he put the lasagne before him, and thereafter ignored her. Which suited Kenda just fine—except she didn't like silences.

Clenching her jaw to stop herself babbling inanely, she watched him from the corner of her eye. A hard-looking man, uncompromising. And extraordinarily attractive. The sort of man she might have liked had circumstances been different. If her reputation hadn't preceded her, which it undoubtedly had, judging by his barbs in the hotel. An *undeserved* reputation. Even if he hadn't seen Richard...

And it wasn't fair! Was it her fault if men found her attractive? No. She didn't *encourage* them, for goodness' sake! Didn't ask to be followed, propositioned... Didn't ask them to sulk, lie about her when all offers were refused. All right, maybe she didn't always need to be scathing, but after years of unwanted attentions politeness was running thin. *Charm* was running thin!

Feeling utterly dispirited, no longer hungry, she pushed away the remains of her lasagne. Life dealt some very cruel blows, she decided. But not to him. Her reputation was in tatters because of something she hadn't even done, whilst his had soared.

Acknowledged as one of the leading experts in the use of ancient weaponry, Carrick's expertise was avidly sought. People came from all over the world to learn how to use sword and longbow, crossbow and mace. He taught them jousting, heraldry, and because of the current trend in historical epics he was much in demand. Perhaps some of his luck would rub off on her. And perhaps it wouldn't.

'Crécy,' Carrick announced as Martin cleared the plates and put coffee before them. 'And stop scowling.'

'Pardon?' she enquired icily.

'Did Richard tell you it was the Battle of Crécy?'

'Yes,' she agreed tersely as she remembered Richard's perfidy. '1346.'

'Then spend the rest of the day finding anything you need. I want it accurate.'

'It will be. How lucky I was early,' she retorted sweetly.

'Yes. You'll find the storerooms on the next floor above the hall. Anything we haven't got, we improvise. One of the storerooms houses a workroom. Whilst we are alone, we eat here. When we have guests, in the hall. We also now try to introduce the food of the period they're researching. One day only. Usually the last day. I'll leave that to you.'

'Thank you,' she said tartly.

'You're the expert. Aren't you?' he asked searchingly.

'Yes. And just to prove it I will organise a banquet for next Friday, the last day of the four-teenth-century guests. The main meal will be at ten. In the morning.'

Martin choked. 'In the morning?' he exclaimed.

'Certainly in the morning. When the lord was in residence, which of course he is,' she added, much too nicely, 'the meal was in the morning and usually lasted two or three hours. It was served with great ceremony. How helpful is the local butcher? Providing there *is* a local butcher,' she derided acidly, 'and I don't have to go out and personally slay my own meat!'

'Don't tempt me,' Carrick warned softly. 'And for a lady in desperate need of a job "conciliatory" might be wise. What will you need?'

'Venison,' she said through her nice white teeth. 'And conciliatory never was, nor probably ever will be, on my curriculum vitae. Hare,' she continued all in the same breath, 'pheasant, partridge, that sort of thing.' And right at that moment she didn't think she even *cared* if he sacked her. 'The ordinary people ate mostly vegetables. Soups, stews. Thick porridge made from peas or beans. There weren't any potatoes then.'

'I'll let you have the butcher's number.'

'Thank you.'

'What about the Romans?'

She gave a saccharine smile. 'Hard biscuit or cake. Cheese, salt, preserved meats. Wine, of course. They liked wine. But they might not have brought any with them.'

'They did,' Carrick said firmly. 'If I have to eat hard biscuit, I definitely need wine to wash it down. And don't tell me *they* ate at ten in the morning.'

'No, but the Britons probably did. In the summer months anyway. I'm more medieval than ancient.'

He grunted, carefully didn't say what he was obviously thinking, finished his coffee and got to his feet. 'I'll be in the armoury if anyone wants me.'

'Shooting yourself?' she asked nicely.

He gave her a look of derision and walked out.

'Chancy,' Martin murmured *sotto voce*.

'He asked for it,' she muttered moodily. 'And I really don't think this is going to work. He doesn't like me. Probably doesn't like women at all!'

'Only in their place,' he murmured, his tongue stuck very firmly in his cheek.

Glancing up, she gave him a smile—a bit strained, a bit sad, but a smile nonetheless. 'Perhaps he's gay.'

'No!' Martin exclaimed, then burst out laughing. 'And his warning about you was obviously right. Trouble with a capital T.'

'Nonsense; I'm very professional.'

'And disruptive.'

'Only if I'm thwarted.' Staring at him, at his lined, humorous face and thinning grey hair, she asked quietly, and just a little bit ominously, 'What warning?'

'Merely that you were trouble,' he replied diplomatically.

'Nothing specific?'

'No. Truly. He merely told me that we would be having a Miss McKinley to stay, that you were an eminent historian—'

'Eminent?' she asked in astonishment. That didn't sound like an accolade Carrick would have given.

'Yes,' he agreed firmly. '"And Martin," he said, "the lady is troublesome. She apparently bends life by the sheer force of her will."'

'Humph. Why *doesn't* he like women?'

'It's not that he doesn't like them but that he doesn't like them on his courses—'

'How very sexist.'

'Because,' he continued firmly, 'we had one here a few months ago, supposedly teaching spinning and weaving.'

'Supposedly?'

'Yes. She spent more time chasing the men than plying her loom, or whatever the expression is, and Carrick swore never again.'

'I don't chase men.'

'I doubt you'd need to! Every man within a mile's radius, whatever his age, will be—'

'Uh-uh,' she cautioned, a sudden bleakness in her lovely eyes. 'I can't help looking like a firework.'

'Delightful is what you look like.' He smiled.

'I'm only delightful on Tuesday,' she said gloomily.

'I look forward to it. A bright, vibrant flame to lure moths,' he added appreciatively.

'Then we'll just have to hope the trainees have gone into their chrysalises!' Shaking her head at a word that might not even exist, she promised, 'And if they haven't I'll wear a bag on my head. Although, if Carrick knew enough about me to give you warning, I would dearly love to know why he let me come.'

'He said you were the best.'

'Obliging of him,' she muttered disagreeably.

Martin gave a small smile, and she gave a shame-faced grin in return. 'Sorry. I just want to kill someone.'

'That bad, huh?'

'Yes,' she agreed tiredly. 'That bad.'

'And Mr Marsh? What do we do about him?'

'Deny him entry? We don't need to tell Carrick.'

'Don't we?'

'No.'

'Why did he need new clothing?'

'My scissors slipped,' she stated flatly. Catching his bitten lip, she gave a reluctant choke of laughter

and sighed. 'I cut up all his clothing,' she confessed. 'Even his shoes. And I'm *glad*! He *hurt* me,
Martin.'

'I'm sorry,' he said gently.

'Yeah.'

With a sympathetic smile that was nearly her un-
doing, he urged, 'Come on; I'll show you up to
your room.'

'I can find it if you give me directions; you look
as though you should be sitting in a rocking-chair,
toasting your feet by the fire. Sorry,' she apologised, her hands thrown up in distress. 'That
sounded rude, and I didn't mean it to be.' Making
an effort—another one—trying so very hard for
normality, she asked, 'Have you been here a long
time?'

'Since I was fourteen. I worked for Carrick's
father.' Opening a door at the far side of the
kitchen, he indicated the stone staircase. 'Follow it
up to the second landing, turn right at the junction,
then left; your room is first on the right. All the
storerooms are on the first landing. Solarium in the
north turret, library below it; the armoury is above
the hall.'

'Heavens.'

'It's not so big you can get lost; all routes
eventually lead back to the great hall. All you need
to remember is that there's a turret at each corner
of the castle, and each turret houses a staircase.
Wander at will; there are no secret rooms—but best
to avoid Carrick's apartment,' he added softly. 'He
might not be too pleased to find you in there.'

'No, I don't suppose he will. Thanks, Martin.
I'll see you later.' Getting to her feet, giving him a

tired smile, Kenda picked up her case and ventured forth. Perhaps life in a castle wouldn't be so grim after all. Certainly Martin was a delight.

Following his directions, she found her room without trouble and moved thankfully inside. It was blessedly warm. Dropping her case, she leaned back against the door and surveyed her domain.

There was a four-poster bed with blue damask curtains, and for two pins, she thought, she would like to climb onto the soft-looking mattress, draw the drapes round her and hide. Soft rugs were scattered on the stone floor; a comfy-looking armchair sat fatly in one corner. The furniture was old, highly polished and probably worth a small fortune. But then, he had a small fortune, or so Richard had said. Richard, the authority on *everything*!

Her mouth a bitter line, she just stood for a moment longer, her eyes bleak. Put it behind you, she told herself. It's over, done with. But it was so *unfair*! And such a shock. She'd trusted Richard. Had thought him her friend. And was she to spend the rest of her life mistrusting people? Waiting and watching for betrayal?

Turning her head, she stared at herself in the long wardrobe-mirror to one side. Such a sad-looking face, she scolded herself. She tried for a smile, and couldn't quite manage it. Life wasn't meant to be like this, she thought unhappily. Life was meant to be enjoyed. She couldn't remember the last time she had enjoyed herself, been carefree.

With a little grimace, she tossed her case onto the bed and began to unpack, and when she'd finished and had arranged her toilet things in the bathroom she tidied herself, exchanged her boots for flat shoes and went exploring.

A bewildering half-hour later she finally got her bearings. Peeking briefly into the library, the store-rooms, the old laundry—presumably kept as a guide for historical accuracy if any of the film-making people that came needed to know the workings—she made her way past the workroom and up into the north turret to the solarium.

It was light and airy, with a magnificent view from all four windows, and she felt like a princess in a fairy tale. A rather tall, troublesome princess.

Smiling sadly at the thought—a smile that made her look quite incredibly vulnerable—her topaz eyes still too bright and full of pain, she stared down at what looked like a stable block. A young lad was walking from stall to stall carrying a bucket. For what reason, she didn't know. She didn't know anything about horses.

Moving to the next window, she stared down at what looked for all the world like a gibbet. Archery practice, she supposed; certainly a lone arrow was sticking out of the torso of one of the hanged 'men'—sacks filled with straw. Craning to the right, she could see a long field. Used for mock tourna-ments, perhaps? Certainly a rail ran down the middle. All very businesslike and profitable. And, from tomorrow, would the world echo to the sound of sword fights? Shouts? Yells of mock battle? Presumably.

Turning away, Kenda stared at the comfortable couches, the table-lamps, the small television in the corner and decided that if she had time she would come up here to read or do research. Out of Carrick's way? she mocked herself.

An abrupt, self-contained man. Ex-army, used to giving orders. And having them obeyed instantly? Tough. She wasn't very good at obeying orders; she preferred giving them. So it was quite likely, wasn't it, that she was going to end up the fly in his well-ordered ointment? Certainly she usually ended up the fly in *someone's*. Steady grey eyes and a mirthless smile. A man of few words—all of them well chosen.

You need the job, she reminded herself. Do at least try to stay on the right side of him. If it hadn't been for Richard...

Mouth tight, she took a deep breath to calm herself. What she needed was advice. Legal advice. Shredding his clothes had been a vengeful reaction to his perfidy; what she needed to do now was think long and carefully about what she could do legally. If he thought she was going to leave it there, then he didn't know her as well as he thought he did. He was going to pay, she promised herself grimly. There would be no more going off half-cocked, no more *reacting*. Especially not to Carrick, she decided. She wouldn't ever give him the chance to level that mocking glance on her again.

Closing the door behind her, resolve quickening her step, her mind busily promoting and discarding ideas for punishing Richard, she descended yet another staircase, and found herself outside what could only be the armoury. Certainly weapons hung or were mounted in every available space. There was no sign of Carrick and, curious, she pushed inside, carefully examined a single-edged sword with a very wide blade that lay on the long table. Picking it up, she made a mock thrust.

'Put it down.'

Startled, she swung round to find Carrick standing in the shadows at the far end of the room, an oily rag in one hand. He looked so right here, she thought inconsequentially, so at home. Long and lithe, impressive—and she was staring, she suddenly realised. Embarrassed, she flicked her eyes away, tried for pleasantness—because if she had to work with him she had to try *something* to mask this peculiar awareness. 'It's a falchion, isn't it?'

'Yes.'

'For next week?'

'And get it ruined?' he derided as he walked towards her. 'No, we use mock-ups only. This is from my private collection.'

'And soothes you in time of trouble? Sorry,' she apologised quickly, with a grimace for her too ready tongue, 'I didn't mean to say that. Are you ever caught out by your students?'

'No.'

'Because they wouldn't know if you made something up?'

'I never make anything up, and I asked you to put it down.'

'I was only—'

'Put it down. It isn't a toy. It's a weapon. A dangerous weapon.'

'And women aren't allowed to play?'

'No.'

'Boadicea did.'

'You aren't the queen of the Iceni.'

'No, just a girl trying to earn an honest buck,' she said quietly as she carefully replaced the falchion.

He looked up, held her with his steady grey eyes. 'Are you?'

'Yes. Martin told me about the other girl. I promise not to chase men.'

'And will you also promise that they won't chase you?'

'Unfair,' she said flippantly, 'because I suspect you know very well that they do. I did tell Martin I could wear a bag on my head.'

His eyes dropped, stared at her exquisite shape, and a rather dry smile tugged at his mouth. 'I doubt even sackcloth and ashes could disguise your—attractions. I have one week in which to teach a lot of...'

'Fools?' she asked helpfully.

'Actors... to at least give the impression they know which end of a sword is which, how to use a pike, an axe, a mace. In short, I do not want them wasting their time—'

'Chasing after me.'

'Correct. Can you ride?'

'No.'

'Then stay away from the stables. Stay away from the practice yard; no important little trips across to your car, or the main gate—'

'I get the message. Is that what the last woman here used to do?'

'Yes.'

'OK. I promise to be good.'

'A promise I intend you to keep. And don't flirt with *me*.'

Tilting her head to one side, anger masked, she asked softly, 'Now, why would I want to do that?'

'Boredom? Because flirting is as natural as breathing to someone like you?'

'The same way as assumptions are natural to you?' she returned pointedly.

'Assumptions based on fact.'

'Gossip,' she corrected him, because no one, in the whole of her life, had ever based their accusations on fact.

He inclined his head in a mocking little gesture that made her want to hit him. Preferably with a sharp implement.

'So what did you hear?'

'Enough.'

'Then why invite me?'

'Richard said you needed a job.'

'Philanthropy?' she queried disbelievingly.

'No. I needed an expert on medieval history. You happen to be one of the best.'

'And you only ever like the best?'

'Yes.'

Studiedly indifferent, she wandered over to the far wall, stared at a loaded crossbow locked in a glass case. Turning to look over her shoulder, she murmured offhandedly, 'I told Martin I thought you might be gay.'

He didn't choke, look outraged, but merely gave a slow smile. 'And would that be a problem?'

'No. Each to his own is what I say.'

'Good. And Richard Marsh?'

'He definitely isn't gay,' she said, with a savagery she couldn't help.

'I'm sure you would know,' he responded
smoothly. 'But is he likely to come here seeking
retribution?'

'I doubt it,' she said as she moved to run her
finger down the smooth wood of a longbow. And
she only knew that Richard wasn't gay because she
knew his wife, *not* from personal experience as
Carrick seemed to think. It was another misconception that he was obviously labouring under. A
misconception he could *stay* labouring under for
all she cared.

'Because if he does,' he continued firmly, 'and
remains as my guest, I will not have my home
turned into a battleground. And leave the bow
alone.'

Removing her finger, she turned to face him and
promised recklessly, 'It won't be. It might be turned
into a mortuary,' she added grimly, 'but I promise
not to stage a battle. What will you do when period
epics are no longer fashionable?'

'Change of subject? I shall try my hand at
farming. No doubt to the amusement and re-
sentment of the locals,' he tacked on.

'What locals? All I've seen so far are sheep! Did
you want to do this?'

'Yes. The arms are my inheritance, and I like
imparting knowledge of their uses.'

'Not to mention the fortune you make whilst you
do so?'

'Why not? If you have a skill, utilise it—and
aren't you supposed to be sorting out uniforms for
tomorrow?'

'Just going.' Definitely not gay, she decided.
Only obdurate.

Waggling her fingers at him, she walked out and quietly closed the door behind her. With a bitter smile, she began to walk along to the storerooms. And Richard *wasn't* likely to come. He wouldn't want a confrontation. Cowards never did. And if she could find a decent lawyer—a *cheap* lawyer, if there was such a thing—she was going to sue him. It wasn't even so much what he had done, although, heaven knew, that was bad enough; it was the fact that he'd cheated her. Deliberately, calculatingly cheated her. That was what she couldn't forgive. And she certainly didn't intend to forget it!

Quietly brooding on Richard's behaviour, on Carrick's, wondering what he did know about her, or thought he knew, she entered the storeroom and began sorting out tunics and mail hosen caps and helms, gauntlets and padded jerkins. Those that needed mending or adapting she carried into the workroom, where she settled herself comfortably and got to work.

Glad as she was to be alone, not to have to make conversation, the hours passed without her knowledge. There were no distractions, no radio, no sounds at all. Quietly thinking her thoughts, grimly promising herself that she would never trust anyone again, that she would take a leaf out of Carrick's book, become remote, distant—although there was a definite temptation to flirt with him just to be aggravating—it took a good few minutes before she became aware of being watched.

Glancing quickly up, she stared at Carrick, waited, felt again that jolt of attraction, and quickly damped it down. 'You wanted me?' she managed quietly.

'No,' he denied lazily. 'Martin sent me to inform you that dinner was ready.'

'Dinner?'

'Yes. It's gone seven.'

'Seven?' she exclaimed in astonishment. 'It *can't* be!'

'But it is. Have you nearly finished?'

'Mmm, just about. Did you say four knights?'

'I did.'

'Then there's enough. Give me five minutes and I'll be down.'

He nodded, walked away, and she let her breath out on a shuddery sigh as she heard his footsteps retreating down the stone stairs, wondering at the little jump her heart had given when she'd seen him standing there. She couldn't *quite* persuade herself that it had been surprise. And that would be clever, she told herself disgustedly—to allow your stupid hormones to ambush your common sense! You've only just finished telling yourself that you'll stay away from men!

With an annoyed little gesture, she broke off her thread, folded the jerkin and laid it with the others. He'd told Martin that she bent life by the force of her will, and never was there more need to do so than now. To bend it away from Carrick. How long had he been watching her? Seconds? Minutes? And what were his thoughts about her?

You don't want to know, she told herself firmly. With a mental shake, she put away her things, washed her hands and walked slowly down to the kitchen—just as Carrick walked out of it. Surprised, she glanced at Martin; he gave a dry smile and indicated that she should look from the window.

With the outside security lights flooding the grounds, it was quite easy to see the car parked on the gravel, a young woman just getting out. Blonde and attractive, late twenties, early thirties, Kenda guessed. And before she could close her door, presumably to come to the castle and knock, Carrick arrived to head her off.

'Why didn't she park in the courtyard?' Kenda asked curiously.

'Because Carrick locks the outer gate at night.'

'Who is she?'

'Lydia,' Martin explained, with an amusement that Kenda didn't altogether understand.

'Who is?'

'On her way out,' he murmured drily.

'Dead but won't lie down?'

'Something like that.'

'She's very attractive.'

'Hard,' he corrected her. 'She runs an art gallery in Lynmouth. Come and sit down; your dinner will get cold. Carrick won't be long.'

Nodding, but for some reason reluctant to abandon her post, she gave a little start when Martin touched her arm, indicated her chair, and with a shamefaced smile she obediently sat down. 'Sorry. I was curious to see how he behaved with other women.'

'Then don't use Lydia as a guide.'

'Who else is there to use?'

'No one at the moment,' he said as he collected her meal and put it before her. 'Roast beef. I hope that's all right?'

'Yes, thanks.' Glancing up as Carrick returned, she said without thinking, 'That was quick.'

He merely looked at her, took his seat.

Feeling snubbed, wishing that for once she could manage to keep her unruly tongue under control, she picked up her knife and fork and asked of whomever wished to answer, 'Would it be all right to use the solarium? When I'm not working, that is.'

'You don't need to sound so defensive,' declared Carrick. 'I have no doubts about your working integrity.'

'No,' she said softly. 'Only my morals.'

He flicked her a glance, a faint, derisive smile in his eyes.

Aggravated, she went on, 'So, can I use it?'

He was silent for a moment, watching her, then nodded. 'Yes. It was my mother's favourite room.'

'Was?'

'Mmm, she died a short while ago.'

'Oh, I'm sorry. What was she like?'

'Lonely,' he said softly and almost inaudibly.

'Because she didn't like the isolation?'

'No, because she missed my father so unbearably.' His tone slightly absent, he laid down his fork and tilted his head in a listening attitude.

'Is something wrong?'

'Possibly not,' he murmured, and then Kenda became aware of the faint sound of an aircraft overhead—an aircraft that didn't sound quite right.

'It sounds—'

'In trouble,' he completed for her. With a swift movement, he got to his feet, bent to take a torch from one of the cupboards and walked out.

Exchanging a glance with Martin, Kenda also abandoned her meal, and followed. It was still drizzling. She should have put a coat on.

The sound was louder now, a throaty roar followed by a cough, after which the engine would cut back in, but they couldn't actually see anything, and it was difficult to pinpoint where the sound was coming from. And then there was a wavering light coming towards them, dipping, rising, dipping, as the pilot fought to keep the plane above the tree line. The engine note was now almost a continuous scream, and Kenda tried frantically to remember how flat the land in front of the castle was.

'He's awfully low—' she began, but Carrick was already moving. Switching on his torch, he broke into a run—just as the engine finally cut out.

CHAPTER TWO

'IF HE can keep it away from those boulders...'
Martin murmured from behind her.

'Boulders?' Kenda asked worriedly.

'Mmm, the ground is littered with them; he
wouldn't be able to see them from up there,
wouldn't be able to see them anyway with the
floodlights blinding him, but... He's turning...
Bloody Norah, he's going to hit the castle! No, no,
we're all right; he's seen Carrick's torch. Should
we ring for an ambulance, do you think?'

'Yes,' said Kenda. 'Even if by some miracle he
manages to land it, he'll need checking over... Oh,
my God!' Wincing as the plane struck the ground
then bounced, she sucked in her breath as though
in sympathy for a mortal wound. 'Go ring!' she
urged Martin. Breaking into a run, she hared
towards the downed plane and Carrick.

'Get away!' he ordered angrily. 'The damned
thing could go up!'

'I'm a first-aider!' she exclaimed breathlessly,
then gave a nervous giggle. She'd always wanted to
say that and no one had ever had an accident near
her before, but she didn't think he was listening as
he ducked under the wing and tried to open the
door.

Not even thinking, she joined him, added her
weight to his. The door came free with a sud-
denness that took them by surprise and they both

fell over backwards. Carrick recovered first and carefully shone his torch into the cockpit; she heard him talk to the pilot.

Scrambling upright, she joined him. 'Don't move him,' she warned hastily.

'He's conscious,' Carrick murmured. 'Head wound, sluggish bleeding, severe gash on right thigh.' He pushed the torch at her, dragged off his sweatshirt, tore it into strips and carefully bound the pilot's leg. 'Can't see any other damage.'

'That doesn't mean there isn't any. Ask him if his back or neck hurts.' Then she asked him herself. Leaning past Carrick's bulk, she gave what she hoped was a reassuring smile. 'Ambulance is on its way. Where are you hurt?'

'Kenda...' Carrick began impatiently.

'No! We need to know if his back is injured. Move out of the way; let me feel.'

'Do you really know what you're doing?'

'Yes.' She hoped.

'All right, but let me undo his harness, check his feet and legs aren't entangled in the wreckage. We might need to move fast.'

When he was ready he moved, eased her in before him, stood ready in case...

Closing her mind to the possibility of fire, an explosion, the oddly insistent creaking noises that the fuselage was making, she gently felt the pilot's spine. She couldn't feel any obvious breaks, but that didn't mean there weren't any. 'Do you have any pain in your neck?' she asked him gently.

He groaned, tried to shake his head until Kenda stopped him, and if Carrick could use his shirt then... Passing him back the torch, she dragged

off her jumper, swiftly twisted it and used it as a
neck brace. 'Keep as still as you can,' she warned.
'If it looks as though it's going to go up we'll get
you out, I promise.' Turning to Carrick, she asked
softly, 'How far does the ambulance have to come?'

'Ten miles. There's a cottage hospital at Lynton,
but whether there's an ambulance there…' Leaving
the sentence hanging, he whispered, 'I'm going to
check the fuel situation.'

She nodded, watched him shine his torch under
the wing above them, then move round to the other
side, where the wing had sheared off and was lying
some distance away. Turning back to the pilot, she
reached for his hand, held it warmly. 'Won't be
long,' she reassured him as she tried to assess any
other damage with her free hand.

He didn't seem to be bleeding anywhere apart
from his head and thigh, and she couldn't feel any
obvious breaks in his legs, but he could go into
shock—that was a real danger—and she wished
she'd thought to ask Martin to bring some blankets.

'Kenda,' Carrick said with desperate quietness
from behind her, 'we need to get him out. Now.'

Her stomach dropped away and she stared at him
blankly, unable for a moment to think, react.
'Right,' she managed over the rapid beating of her
heart.

'Keep his head as still as you can,' he instructed.
His voice calm, competent, his eyes steady on hers,
she believed utterly that they would be able to do
this. 'I'll try to lift him in the position he's in. All
right?'

'Yes,' she agreed, in a voice too small to be heard.

'Take the torch.'

'Right.'

'Ready?'

'Yes.'

Shoving the torch into the waistband of her skirt, she held the pilot's head firmly between her palms, swallowed, took a deep breath, edged as far to the side as she could as Carrick bent, pushed one arm beneath the pilot's legs, the other round his back, and lifted. With a grunt of effort, he staggered backwards, Kenda still supporting the injured man's head, just as the first lick of fire appeared.

Within seconds, the lick had become a flame, and with a whoosh of igniting vapour the whole plane went up like a torch. The blast staggered them, heat seared them, but they didn't drop the pilot. And then Martin was there with a thick blanket, helping to lower the injured man to the ground on his side, in the same position in which they'd rescued him from the plane.

'Close,' Carrick murmured laconically.

'Yes,' she agreed shakily.

'Are you all right?'

'Yes.'

'Not hurt?'

'No. You?'

'No.'

She tried for a smile, found that her mouth wouldn't obey. Hands braced on her knees, she bent to draw great gulps of air into her lungs.

'Should I take the four-wheel drive to meet the ambulance?' Martin asked. He sounded very, very shaken.

'Yes,' Carrick agreed. 'If it gets bogged down . . . Drive slowly, carefully . . .'

'I will.'

'He needs something to do,' Carrick explained quietly. 'And I told you to stay clear. Don't you ever do anything you're told?'

'No,' she replied, because it sometimes seemed that she didn't. Turning to look at the burning plane, she shuddered, turned back, found him watching her. 'What?' she queried. 'Why are you looking at me like that?'

He gave a faint smile, shook his head. 'Nothing. Let's have the torch.'

Handing it over, still puzzled by the way he'd been staring at her, she watched as he bent to examine the pilot, shone the beam carefully over his face, then held back the blanket for a moment whilst he examined his makeshift bandage.

Rain slicked his naked back; it was smooth, and long, and shapely. A back that invited touch. And she clenched her hands tight to stop herself doing anything so foolish. Shock, she tried to tell herself, but she knew it wasn't only that. From the first moment she'd seen him, she had wanted to touch him. His behaviour had made her deny those feelings, but denial didn't mean they didn't exist.

Flickering shadows from the burning plane played over him, distorted him, and that funny little pain began inside—that funny little pain she had felt when she'd seen him standing in the doorway of the hotel bedroom. Not having had the time then to think about it, she examined her feelings now— that odd yearning to touch, be touched, fulfilled, instead of always being on the defensive, the little jump her heart had given when she'd found him standing over her in the workroom, the now disturbing insight that if they did touch, love it would be a perfect union.

But he knew about her—he'd said so—suspected her morals, and so she was never likely to learn the secrets of his body, only his contempt. And it was all foolish anyway; she didn't know him. But it was odd, to feel like this; they were feelings she had never felt before.

A breath of wind explored her near nakedness and she gave a little shiver, suddenly aware of how cold she was. Her flimsy bra was already soaked and sticking wetly to her skin, and she hugged her arms round herself for warmth as she stared off towards the track, prayed for the ambulance as her teeth began to chatter.

'Go inside,' Carrick urged. 'You'll catch your death standing there like that.'

'No.' She didn't want to go inside; in fact it seemed vitally important that she remain with Carrick and the pilot. Here on a windy and rain-swept moor, with a downed plane, and Carrick, quietly competent, a dark, crouching figure who seemed entirely in his element.

'Here it is!' she exclaimed thankfully as she saw the blue light begin to emerge from the tree line. Carrick's Land Rover was heading out on a converging course, and within minutes both vehicles were pulling up in front of them. The paramedics jumped down, glanced at the plane, and one had a brief word with Carrick whilst the other bent to examine the pilot. Her jumper was exchanged for a proper neck brace and handed back to her with a smile.

'Thanks, miss; well done. You all right, Carrick?'

'Fine. My sweatshirt you can keep.'

The man laughed. A stretcher was fetched, and they all helped load the pilot carefully onto it. 'We'll let you know how he does.'

'Thanks.'

Rain slicking them, all three watched and waited until the ambulance was out of sight. 'Let's go,' Carrick ordered softly. He helped Martin and then her in, climbed behind the wheel of the Land Rover and drove them back to the castle. Kenda still held her jumper bundled in her arms. It hadn't seemed worth putting it back on.

Instead of heading back to the kitchen, he led them upstairs. There was a smear of mud on his back, and without thinking she put out her hand, wiped it away.

Turning quickly, as though startled, he stared at her.

'Mud,' she explained weakly as she held out her fingers for him to see. 'I didn't—wasn't . . .'

'Taking advantage of a naked back?'

'No. I don't even like you.'

'You barely even know me.'

'I don't have to. I made up my mind *instantly*!'

He laughed, pushed open the door to his quarters and ushered them inside. Know him? No. But at that moment she knew that she wanted to.

'A lady of impulse.'

'Mmm?' she queried absently.

'I said, A lady of impulse.'

'Oh, yes.'

'An impulse that could have got you killed.'

'For touching a naked back?'

'No, disobeying orders.' Leaving them, he walked into his bedroom, and she stared at nothing, remembered his behaviour at the plane. They had enjoyed a small parcel of closeness born of danger, and now everything seemed flat, grey, one-dimensional. He was back within minutes, a dark sweatshirt pulled on over his naked chest. Negligently tossing another to Kenda, he ordered her almost tersely, 'Cover yourself.'

Flushing, because it had sounded as though he thought she was flaunting her near-nakedness on purpose, she struggled into the sweatshirt, shivered as it touched her chilled skin, then watched him cross to the bar and pour generous measures of brandy for them all. A strong, attractive man. Competent and negligently caring.

Handing them a glass each, he told Martin to go and have a hot bath.

'Don't I rate the same concern?' she asked quietly, when Martin had gone and she was nursing her drink in front of a roaring fire.

'No, you're younger, fitter, and I want to talk to you.'

'About disobeying orders?'

'No,' he denied, and surprisingly he smiled. 'I rarely repeat myself, but if I'm ever in an accident,' he added softly, 'I hope you're nearby. And especially wearing some very fetching underwear.'

Astonished, she just stared at him. '*That's* what you wanted to talk about?'

'No.'

'But that's why you were staring at me so strangely at the plane?'

He hesitated, shrugged, murmured, 'Maybe. Drink your brandy.' Returning to the bar, he collected his own.

With a bewildered little shake of her head, she looked around her. They were in a large room, with long cream sofas facing each other across the hearth, an expensive-looking rug between. A heavy, ornate dining table and four chairs took up another corner of the room, there were a couple of armchairs, heavy cream curtains at the window and a small balcony, she saw.

'You are allowed to sit,' he commented quietly. He sounded amused.

With a little shrug, she perched on the end of the sofa nearest her. 'This is nice.'

'You mean you can find nothing wrong with my taste in furnishings?'

'No,' she sighed, 'and stop baiting me. Will the pilot be all right, do you think?'

'Hopefully. They'll ring tomorrow.'

She nodded, then exclaimed in bewilderment, 'I can't even believe we *did* that! Perhaps no one ever believes they will die.'

'No,' he agreed. 'It was a brave thing to do.'

'No, it wasn't,' she contradicted him awkwardly. 'I wasn't even thinking.'

'And you *are* a first-aider,' he teased.

'As you are, I suspect. That was a very competent bit of bandaging you did back there.'

'Mmm,' he agreed wryly. 'I had to take a course when I became a volunteer ranger for the Park.'

'Park?'

'Exmoor. It's one of twelve extensive areas of England and Wales selected for special protection.

It's looked after by the Exmoor National Park Authority. We have a duty to "protect the beauty and character of the area and facilitate its quiet enjoyment by the public",' he quoted somewhat drily.

'*Quiet* enjoyment?' she queried with a smile.

'Usually. We don't normally have light aircraft dropping in. Is this your first visit?'

'Mmm.'

'And not seeing it at its best.'

'I doubt that would make a difference.' Warm now, a bit achy, she listened to the silent room, the soft crackle of the flames in the hearth—and that overwhelming awareness she'd felt by the plane returned in full measure, and so she babbled, used words to fill all the spaces in her mind so that she wouldn't, couldn't think. 'I like cities, big cities; the countryside makes me feel—exposed. All that open space, fresh air; not my scene, I'm afraid.'

'You get used to it. I wouldn't want to live anywhere else now.'

'But don't you miss theatres? Shops? *People?*'

'There are theatres and shops here.'

'But not within walking distance!'

'No, but it's no hardship to drive. And there are people. I have neighbours.'

'You do? Where?'

He smiled again, a smile she was beginning to watch for, wait for—and that was not only stupid but dangerous. 'The farm's under a mile away, where Jason and his parents live.'

'Jason?'

'He looks after the horses. And in under two miles in *that* direction—' he pointed '—is another farm.'

'But if there's an accident or anything, if you need help in a hurry—'

'There are telephones,' he pointed out drily.

'There might be a power failure.'

'What a pessimist you are.'

She watched him, watched the shadows from the fire play across his strong face, his relaxed body as he came to sit opposite, then stared down into her drink. 'Do you miss the army?'

'No,' he answered simply. 'And why are you so nervous all of a sudden?'

'I'm not,' she denied quickly, with that ready hauteur she used to such good effect to keep people at a distance.

'Afraid of being alone with me?'

'Don't be absurd.'

Leaning back, he crossed his long legs, nursed his own brandy in large palms and watched her. 'Leave Martin alone,' he warned softly.

'Leave Mar...? Are you *mad*?' she snapped up her head to exclaim.

'Not to my knowledge,' he said easily.

'Then don't make such stupid remarks. He's old enough to be my father! What do you think I am? Some sort of—*predator*?'

'Yes.'

'Well, I'm not! And I don't pursue men. Of *any* age!'

'You pursued Richard.'

'I did *not*! And did you *have* to spoil it?'

'Spoil what?'

'*This!* I had just managed to *forget* Richard!' Getting to her feet, cross all over again, hurt, she gulped back her brandy. 'Thank you for the drink,' she added flatly. Plonking her glass on the mantelshelf, she turned to go.

'Sit down,' he ordered softly.

'I don't want to sit down. I'm going to bed. I don't like people who are so insufferably *smug*! And I certainly,' she whirled round to continue, 'don't intend to sit here and be insulted! You know absolutely nothing about me! Know—'

'I wasn't insulting you,' he interrupted, 'and I know a great deal about you. I know that you were a brilliant student, that you're passionately interested in history—'

'That I have a terrific body!' she put in waspishly.

He gave a mocking little inclination of his head before continuing, 'That men like you—and that you can be extraordinarily troublesome.'

'I am not *troublesome*!'

'Cutting up Richard's clothing wasn't troublesome?'

'No. It was deserved!'

'And breaking up Peter Dawson's marriage?'

Staring at him, tawny eyes narrowed so that she looked like an angry cat, she stated, 'I did *not* break up his marriage! *He* did!'

'Because of the affair he had with you.'

'We did not have an affair!' she denied angrily. 'And if you had bothered to ask *me* instead of listening to nasty rumours you would have known that!'

'I didn't know you,' he said mildly.

'Nor do you now!'

His smile was soft, disbelieving. 'You lost your job at the museum because of it.'

'I lost my job because of his damned fantasy,' she corrected him icily. 'The "affair" was only in his head!'

'And everyone else's.'

'And is that *my* fault?'

'I don't know. And it wasn't the only rumour I heard about you.'

'Wasn't it?' she asked derisively.

'No.'

'So what else did you hear?'

He gave a small smile.

'*Well?*'

'I was told that you were—predatory.'

'By whom?'

'James Lincoln.'

'James Lincoln?' she exclaimed, incensed. Marching back to tower over him, she snarled, 'Let me tell you about *James Lincoln*! He doesn't have a casting couch, he has a whole . . . bed shop! Prostitution would be a safer alternative to coming anywhere near James Lincoln! That man is sleaze at its worst! So don't talk to me about James Lincoln!'

'Propositioned you, did he?'

'Oh, not only propositioned,' she informed him furiously. 'Pawed me, insulted me, lied about me!'

'And what did you cut up of his?' he asked in amusement, his head tilted back in order to see her face.

'I know what I'd have liked to have cut up! Unfortunately, I didn't have my scissors on me!'

'So what did you do?'

'Stole his precious car then posted the keys back to him and told him to find it!'

'His *Lamborghini*?' Carrick demanded incredulously.

'No, he had a Ferrari! And it wasn't *my* fault if joyriders took it after I'd parked it, was it?'

He choked, then began to laugh. 'Where did you park it?'

'Scotland,' she said shortly.

'*Scotland?* You drove from London to *Scotland* to park it?'

'Yes.'

'Did he ever get it back?'

'Not in one piece,' she said sweetly. 'Goodnight.'

Still laughing, he echoed softly, 'Goodnight.'

Opening the door, she came face to face with a young man with untidy black hair. An extraordinarily agitated young man.

'I've been wandering around this bloody castle for hours!' he exclaimed furiously. 'Where the hell is everyone?'

'Here,' Carrick replied mildly, still lounging comfortably on the sofa. 'Who are you?'

'David Healy. There's a burned plane out front,' he said accusingly as though they'd put it there to thwart him. 'I was nearly run off the road by an ambulance! I've been ringing and ringing that ridiculous bell you have! There was no answer and so I came in,' he added with a defiance that nearly matched Kenda's. 'I've been up and down blasted staircases, in and out of chambers—'

'Why? You aren't due until tomorrow.'

'I know I'm not due until tomorrow,' he retorted as he strode past Kenda and went to warm his hands ostentatiously by the fire, 'but because of the

weather we thought we'd better come early in case
we couldn't get through.'

'Get *through*? This is Devon, not Outer
Mongolia! And what do you mean, *we*?'

'All of us! They're following behind. The hotel's
flooded. The wall holding the river back collapsed.
No light, no heating, no kitchen—so we thought
we'd better come here.'

'You mean they're all coming here to *sleep*? I
don't have the facilities to sleep eight people!'

'Four.'

'What?'

'There are only four of us. The others managed
to find another hotel. Sorry,' he muttered. Glancing
at Kenda, who still hovered in the doorway, he gave
a lame smile, belatedly registered her extraordinary
beauty, and his face brightened. 'Hello. You must
be Kenda. How are you?'

'Never mind how Kenda is! Tell me how I'm
supposed to sleep four extra people!'

Reluctantly dragging his attention away from
Kenda, David explained, 'The hotel's given us
blankets...'

'Wonderful. What are we supposed to put them
on?'

'You must have plenty of spare rooms here.'

'Oh, yes, plenty; they also have stone floors.'

'Oh.'

The silence lengthened and both Kenda and
David stared at Carrick, who from being mildly
amused now looked extremely aggravated. Why?
Kenda wondered. There were other guest rooms—
she'd seen them when she'd been exploring—and
people must have stayed here before.

'Any chance of a drink?' David asked eventually.

'What? Oh, yes. Sorry. Help yourself.'

Whilst David went across to help himself to a large Scotch, Carrick began drumming his fingers on the arm of the sofa, mouth pursed in thought.

'Who's coming?'

'Hmm? Oh, another knight and a bowman.'

'And the others are where?'

'Simonsbath.'

Carrick nodded. 'And the other one?'

'What?'

'You said four were coming here.'

'Oh, yes,' he agreed with a grimace. 'Ellen.'

There was a tiny silence. 'Ellen?' Carrick enquired softly.

'Yes. Ellen Marks.'

'Ellen *Marks*?'

'Yes,' David agreed.

'No.'

'What?' he queried in confusion.

'No. I am not having that woman here.'

'But she—'

'No,' Carrick repeated, and then all in the same breath added, 'Martin, why are you hovering barefoot in the doorway?'

Swinging around, Kenda stared at him, then gave a small smile.

'Looking for lost sheep,' Martin retorted pithily. 'I heard the bell, but I didn't think that even you would expect me to climb out of the bath and rush naked just to answer the door.'

'No, I wouldn't. Go and put something on your feet. Or, better still, go to bed.'

'And miss all the fun? No, thank you. Why are you early?' he asked David.

'The hotel is apparently flooded,' Carrick informed him.

'Not "apparently",' David put in. 'Is.'

'*Is* flooded,' Carrick corrected himself with a little dip of his head. 'And so we have four extra guests.'

'For the *week*?'

'Yes.'

'No,' David replied at the same time. 'We'll be leaving Friday morning. Sorry. They're cutting back on expenses.'

Getting to his feet, placing his brandy glass on the mantelshelf next to Kenda's, Carrick said drily, 'And I'm to teach you in four days how to win a battle?' Shaking his head at the stupidity of financiers, he offered, 'The three men can share Kenda's room. Ellen can have the other one.'

'I'm not sharing my room with three men!' Kenda responded in scandalised accents. 'Whatever you may think of my morals, I—'

'Too much for you?' Carrick interrupted, with just the faintest twitch to his lips.

'Carrick,' she warned tightly.

He smiled, shook his head at her. 'I didn't intend you to sleep with them.'

'Then where *am* I supposed to sleep? The storeroom?'

'No, the dressing room off my bedroom.'

'The...? Oh, no,' she said forcefully as she felt the oddest, most peculiar sliding sensation in her tummy. 'I'm not sharing *your* room either.'

'I didn't ask you to. The dressing room is quite separate.'

'Then let David use it.'

'No.'

'I am *not* using it!' she stated firmly.

'Then you'll have to share with Ellen.'

About to agree, she hesitated. 'What's she like?' she asked suspiciously.

He gave a grim smile.

'*Not* spinning and weaving?' she asked softly.

'The very same.'

'But you said you wouldn't have her back, gave her as the reason you didn't want women here!'

'Not to you I didn't,' he denied with an under-browed glance at Martin.

Martin shrugged. 'She thought you might be gay.'

David choked, and they all looked at him. 'Don't look at me! It wasn't *my* fault she came! Anyway, she's not *like* a woman. Apparently she's changed.' His expression intimated that it wasn't for the better.

'Changed?'

'Yes,' he muttered. 'She doesn't like men. Doesn't think we're needed.'

'Needed?' Carrick exclaimed. 'For what?'

'Anything.'

'The end of the world is nigh?' he queried in amusement. 'What about procreation? No, no, don't tell me. Sperm banks?'

'Yes. And...er...'

'Well, go on, spit it out; might as well have it all.'

'She's to be one of the bowme—persons,' he concluded in a rush.

'Bow persons,' Carrick repeated slowly. 'Women didn't fight at the Battle of Crécy,' he pointed out.

'I know. It's symbolic.'

'Symbolic,' Carrick echoed with a little nod. 'I see. And I'm to teach her to use the bow, am I?'

'Yes.'

'No.'

'What?'

'No,' he repeated. 'I don't train women.'

'That's sexist.'

'I still don't train them.'

'But she'll be furious!'

'Fury I can cope with.' Glancing at Kenda, he gave a slow smile. 'Want to share with her? I'm sure you'd get on famously. You'd have so much in common.'

'No,' Kenda said. 'Despite your sexist rules.' Which was odd, because normally sexist remarks had her espousing any number of causes. But not in this case, and not with Ellen. Because she didn't care? Because she wasn't the one being forbidden? How very selfish.

'Wise.' David nodded gloomily. 'She's politically correct. By the end of the week she'd have you leatherless . . .'

They all looked at David's shoes, and he squirmed uncomfortably, trying to hide his man-made uppers from view. 'It was easier to give in,' he explained gloomily. 'She goes on so. Barring one or two diehards, the whole film set's become green, biodegradable, meatless. Make-up isn't allowed for cosmetic purposes . . .'

'Allowed?' Kenda asked softly.

'Mmm. That is one very forceful young woman.'

'So is Kenda,' Carrick pointed out drily. 'So?' he asked her. 'What's it to be?'

'I'm almost tempted,' she began thoughtfully. 'But no, all things considered, I think I might be safer with you.' And if her heart gave an extra little thump no one knew but her.

'So do I,' Martin agreed. 'I'll go and make sure the rooms are ready,' he told Carrick, then beckoned to David. 'You can help me rearrange beds.'

When they'd gone, with some reluctance on David's part, Kenda continued to stare at Carrick. 'She wasn't chasing other men,' she accused him almost under her breath. 'She was chasing you.'

He inclined his head. 'But thankfully, it would seem, no longer.'

'Yet you had the cheek to accuse *me* of causing mayhem?'

'Mmm, it does seem rather unfair, doesn't it? Shall we move your belongings? And this is *not* an invitation.'

'I didn't for one moment suppose it was.'

'Good. Let's go.'

Bundling up everything in her room, they carried it along the landing and dumped it in the small dressing room. 'She might think . . .'

'Yes,' he agreed.

'Which was your plan all along?'

'I can't help what she thinks.'

'Liar,' she said softly.

He smiled. 'Look on it as first aid. Or preventive medicine.'

'You don't believe she's off men? Or do you think she might change her mind when she sees you again?'

'Always best to be prepared, don't you think?' he asked blandly.

'So you want me to *encourage* her?'

'To think of you as my mistress? Yes. I'm sure you can be extraordinarily fearsome if you put your mind to it. In fact, I've witnessed firsthand your fearsome behaviour.'

With the disquieting thought that she was probably going mad, she began hanging her things in the wardrobe. Carrick sat on the bed and watched her. Unsettled her. And how, she wondered, had they come from accusations to alliance in such a short space of time? And, however foolish it might be, the thought of being so near to him excited her.

'Fearsome, huh?'

'Dragon-like. A veritable lioness!'

'And which room will Miss Marks use?'

'The one that's furthest away from me.'

'Barred?' she asked softly.

'Sadly, no.' The subject obviously finished with, he continued, 'We'll have to share the bathroom, I'm afraid.'

'No problem.'

'You'll be quite safe,' he added.

'I never doubted it for a moment.'

'Will *I*?' he tacked on softly.

'Frying pan to fire? A bit late for regrets.'

'No regrets, just native caution. I'd better ring Mary, warn her of the changed circumstances.'

'Mary?

'Jason's mother,' he explained with his bland smile. 'She comes in to cook and clean when we have trainees here. She lives on the farm.'

'Yours?'

'Mmm. You can manage?'

'Sure. I'm a big girl now.'

'I know. I noticed.'

Their eyes met, held, and he gave a derisive smile that hurt, before turning away. Disappointed, scathing of her own stupidity, because she'd been enjoying their little exchange, she went to put her toilet things in the bathroom.

'Is there anything else we need to organise?' he asked some half an hour later.

'Soap, extra towels?'

He nodded. 'Get a list going, will you?'

'Aye, aye, Captain.'

'Major,' he corrected her absently. 'We will also need to alter the schedule. No banquet Friday night.'

'No.'

'And that reminds me . . .' Walking across to the bureau in the corner, he took out a key and handed it to her. 'This door is to be kept locked at all times. Hang this round your neck or something, but don't lose it.'

'Oh, come on, that's a bit excessive, isn't it?'

'No, it isn't, and if she's as fanatical as David thinks I don't want her in here throwing out anything she considers politically incorrect. Like leather.'

Tucking the key into her pocket, she asked curiously, 'Apart from Ellen, why didn't you want

them staying here? I've never seen anyone so reluctant to house guests.'

'I like my privacy.'

'For what?' she laughed. 'Orgies?'

'Of course orgies,' he agreed smoothly. 'I'll go
and see how Martin is getting on.' He pulled open
the door and found Martin outside, hand raised
ready to knock, hair now combed, feet safely shod.

'They're here,' he announced portentously.

'Right.' Staring at the elderly man for a few moments in silence, he suddenly smiled. 'Is it too
much?'

Martin shook his head. 'There's life in the old
dog yet.'

'I never doubted it. Another adventure? I like
adventures.'

'Could be the best one yet.' Glancing at Kenda
as she hovered behind Carrick, Martin grinned.
'*Definitely* could be the best one yet. Ready to meet
the famous Ellen?' he asked her.

Somewhat puzzled by their conversation, she
nodded. 'I can't wait.'

'Then come along,' Carrick encouraged her. 'I
want you at my side.'

'Like your lady?'

'Like glue. Ellen Marks is one very thick-skinned
woman. Or was. Hang onto my arm.'

'Why? Think she might try to snatch you away?'

'No, it looks better.'

'It looks contrived!'

'I don't care.'

'If your friends could see you now,' she par-
odied softly.

Turning his head, he surveyed her from his slightly superior height. 'Pardon?'

'Your army friends. If they could see you now. The brave major hiding behind a woman's skirts.'

'Who said I was brave?'

'Weren't you?'

He shrugged, tugged her forward, and when they entered the hall, Kenda dutifully hanging onto his arm, she whispered softly, 'Should I simper?'

'No.'

With a wry smile, she stepped out into the hall with him. David and two other rather anxious-looking young men stared back—and one lone female, who didn't look anxious at all, just . . . recycled. Thin and plain, with a rather discontented expression, she wore a long black coat that had seen better days, plimsolls and granny glasses. Her red hair could have been pretty—if she'd allowed it to be. It was scrapped back with what looked like a piece of string, which was tied incongruously in a bow.

'*That's* Ellen Marks?' she demanded, too low for anyone else to hear.

'Yes.'

'But she's . . .'

'Plain, yes. Don't let that fool you. In my experience, the plainer the woman, the more aggressive she usually is—except in your case, of course.'

'I'm not aggressive,' she denied absently as she continued to stare at Ellen Marks. 'You do like to put labels on people, don't you? I know some very *nice* plain women.'

'So do I. Ellen Marks isn't one of them.'

Whilst Carrick introduced himself she continued to stare curiously at Ellen Marks, who was watching Carrick. Avidly.

'So we'll meet here at 0800—sharp! We have a lot to get through and very little time to do it. I will contact the others at the hotel, make sure they know the arrangements. In the meantime, whilst Martin shows you to your rooms, I'll get some tea and sandwiches organised. And I would be grateful if you would remember that this is my home. Understood?'

There was a chorus of yesses, assurances of obedience, and he finally nodded, apparently satisfied that they would obey. Except, of course, for Ellen Marks, who apparently didn't obey anybody. A bit like herself?

Still attached to his arm, she accompanied Carrick back to the kitchen, trying very hard to stifle her laughter. 'Such a hard taskmaster,' she said softly.

'One must have rules. People like rules.'

'Except Ellen.'

'Yes,' he agreed, the grimness returning. 'Except Ellen.'

'Well, that's the first hurdle over!' David exclaimed from behind them. 'I'm sure everything will be fine.' He sounded nervous.

'I'm glad to hear it,' Carrick murmured. Handing him a knife, he ordered, 'Get buttering. Kenda, make the tea.'

'Yes, sir.'

His lips twitched as he gave David a sidelong look. 'Have you told Miss Marks she can't be a bow person?'

'Not yet.'

'Then I suggest you do so before the morning.'

'Can't you tell her?' he pleaded. 'Say it's because of insurance or something?'

'No.'

With an aggrieved look, David snatched the knife and began plastering butter on the bread as though he hated it.

'How long has she been an actress?' Carrick asked curiously as he took meat, cheese and tomatoes from the fridge.

'She isn't. She's a production assistant.'

'Then why does she need to learn how to shoot?'

'Because she's Ellen!' he stated crossly. 'Because she's a friend of the director! And because between them they decided to make everything politically correct! Anyway, I thought you would have known all this. You've obviously met before.'

'Yes, before her conversion.'

'She chased him,' Kenda put in helpfully.

Carrick gave her a derisive look. 'Stick to the point. Whose idea was it to come here to learn?' he asked David.

Staring at him, obvious thought processes going on behind his brown eyes, David queried slowly. 'You mean, she wangled it? Because of you? You don't think she's changed?'

'Got it in several. Who's the director?'

Clearly intrigued, David murmured with absent gloom, 'Claire Potter. But a job's a job.'

Biting her lip to stop her laughter, Kenda made the tea in the largest pot she could find, assembled the mugs on a tray, added sugar and milk.

'Carry the tray through for Kenda, will you, David?'

'Why can't you do it?'

'Ellen might pounce,' Kenda giggled. Both men looked at her, and she turned quickly away, stifling laughter.

When David had gone, she gave in to her hilarity. 'Oh, my. Poor David.'

'Stop laughing; it isn't remotely funny.'

'Yes, it is. Alas, poor Carrick, I knew him well.'

The door opened, and Ellen walked in. 'I came to help,' she stated assertively.

CHAPTER THREE

'NO!' THEY denied in unison.

'Don't be silly,' Ellen said. 'Many hands make light work.'

'Not in my kitchen, they don't,' Kenda argued firmly.

'*Your* kitchen?'

'Yes.'

'I thought you were the historian.'

'I am, amongst other things. Thank you for the offer, but really, we can manage.'

'Don't be silly,' she repeated. Advancing to stand beside Carrick, she put a hand on his arm, stared at him and stated bluntly, 'I have no wish to discuss my behaviour when I was here before.'

'Must be catching,' Carrick murmured, with a swift glance at Kenda.

'I beg your pardon?'

'Private joke. You were saying?'

'That I'm a different person.'

'I'm very glad to hear it.'

'I didn't speak earlier,' she continued determinedly, 'because I didn't want to embarrass you in front of the others.'

'I don't get embarrassed. And whatever game you've decided to play, don't,' he warned.

'I don't know what you mean.'

'Don't you?' Dislodging her hand, he pointed to the sandwich filling. 'You want to help? Help.'

'Not with *meat*,' she declared as she pushed it distastefully aside. 'Salad?'

'Don't have any.'

'I'm vegan.'

'Still don't have any.'

She sighed. 'Are the tomatoes organic?'

'I've no idea.'

The sigh deepened. '*I* insisted they come here to learn; don't make me regret that, Carrick.'

'Why?'

'What?' she queried in confusion.

'*Why* did you insist?'

'Because you're the best, of course. What other reason could there be?'

'You tell me. No, on second thoughts, don't. Behave yourself and we'll get on just fine. The bread's already buttered.'

With a distasteful shudder, she pushed it to one side and began slicing tomatoes before putting them between slices of dry bread. Glancing up, seeing Kenda watching her, she gave her a look of dislike. 'Butter is animal fat, and apart from the moral question it's very bad for the arteries.' Looking Kenda's rather magnificent figure up and down, she added nastily, 'You look as though you could afford to lose some weight.'

Ignoring Carrick's glance of warning, Kenda gave her a sweet smile, then jumped when he rescued the buttered bread and slapped it down in front of her. Indicating the sliced beef, his grey eyes holding hers, he ordered, 'Fill.'

Her mouth twisted in a wry smile.

'Carrick,' Ellen reproved him, 'we're all vegan.'

'I'm not,' Kenda denied softly.

'Then you're a very silly girl.'

'Neither is Carrick.'

'Then I shan't be surprised to hear that he's had a heart attack in the not too distant future.'

Glancing at Carrick, who, according to Ellen, ate all the wrong things, and looked the picture of health, and then at Ellen, who presumably ate all the right things, and looked anaemic, she shook her head. 'Then why don't you make all the sandwiches for your lot and let me make ours? Are you really off men?' she couldn't resist asking.

'They have their place, no doubt,' Ellen admitted magnanimously, then gave a smile sweeter than any Kenda had so far managed. 'Probably yours.'

There was a startled silence, and then Carrick gave the most infectious little hiccup of laughter that Kenda thought she had ever heard. 'A hit,' he said softly.

Staring at him, then at Ellen, Kenda's lips twitched, and she burst out laughing. If Ellen had laughed, or even smiled, they could have been friends for life, because Kenda did so like people with quick wits, but she didn't, merely looked astonished, then disgruntled.

'I shan't give up,' she warned frostily. 'I should hate to be responsible for ill health when I could have prevented it.'

'Not to worry,' Carrick informed her kindly, his mouth still quirking slightly. 'Kenda's a first-aider.' With a small smile for Martin when he walked in, he asked, 'Take these through, would you?'

Martin glanced curiously from one to the other, shrugged, nodded, picked up the plate of beef sandwiches and walked out.

'You shouldn't have servants,' Ellen pointed out. 'It's morally wrong. People have the right to be free.'

'Sorry to disappoint you, Ellen,' he drawled softly, 'but I'm not free, and *my* services don't come cheap. They wish to learn warfare? They pay.'

'We,' she corrected him. '*We*. I also wish to learn. Didn't David tell you?'

'Yes.'

'And?'

'No.'

'No?' she queried haughtily. 'You're being employed.'

'But not as a servant,' he returned. 'And not by you.'

'Then perhaps I ought to tell you that if I can't learn neither will they.'

'Fine,' he agreed, unperturbed. 'You can all leave when you've eaten.'

Staring at him, her mouth pinched, she stated disbelievingly, 'You don't mean that.'

'Don't I?' Picking up an apple from the table, he tossed it negligently in his hand, then bit deep into the juicy flesh before walking after Martin. Kenda quickly followed, stifling her laughter.

The crew ate dry tomato sandwiches, and looked miserable.

'I'm sorry you won't be staying,' Carrick announced, to stares of astonishment and disbelief. 'I don't give arms training to women,' he explained, 'and Ellen informs me that if I don't teach

her she will leave, and that if *she* leaves you all have
to. You're very welcome to use the telephone to ring
in search of a hotel.'

'No!' David exclaimed, and after the ensuing
babble, arguments ranging back and forth whilst
Carrick watched with an amused smile on his face,
the consensus of opinion was that they stay.

'Then I'm staying too,' Ellen announced. 'I will
observe.'

'From a window,' Carrick stated.

'What?'

'From a window,' he repeated. 'No one, but no
one, is allowed in the exercise yard whilst I'm
training. It's too dangerous.'

'Then I will observe from a window!' she agreed
angrily. Getting to her feet, she flounced off and
up the stairs.

'You've just made yourself an enemy,' David observed quietly.

Carrick looked unmoved.

An hour later, they finally made it back to his
quarters. Walking across to the bar, he held up the
Scotch in query and, when Kenda shook her head,
poured himself a large one. 'I'm not entirely sure
I can take four days of being improved.'

'More like four days of her trying to kill you.'

'Killing is politically incorrect,' he said drily.
'Glad you aren't sharing a room with her?'

'Fervently.'

He gave a small smile. 'Go to bed. Tomorrow is
going to be a long day. And do *try* not to come to
blows with her!'

'Verbal fencing only,' she promised. 'Goodnight.' Pushing into his bedroom, she heard the

outer door open behind her, halted and looked back.

'I want to talk to you,' Ellen declared. Catching sight of Kenda, she added pointedly, 'Alone.'

'You stay, I stay,' Kenda said softly.

'Why?' she scoffed. 'Don't you trust him?'

'No. He might be tempted to strangle you,' Kenda added with a kind smile.

Turning her back on her, Ellen demanded, 'Why is she here?'

'Lovers' tryst,' Carrick drawled.

'You aren't lovers.'

'Aren't we?'

'No.' She looked at Kenda. Kenda looked back, remained silent. She wasn't sure why. 'I need to talk to you. In private.'

'Is it desperate?' he asked mildly. 'Is the castle on fire? Someone dying?'

'No.'

'Then it can wait until the morning. My hours of business are between eight and six. Goodnight, Ellen.'

'But it's urgent!'

'Life-threatening?'

'No,' she denied crossly. 'I have one or two points I wish to discuss.'

'Make a list,' he encouraged her. 'Give it to me tomorrow.'

She glared at him, glared at Kenda, then gave a very nasty smile. 'Perhaps you should remember,' she told him, 'that Kenda's lovers tend to end up dead.'

'Or decimated,' he added softly as Ellen turned on her heel and stalked away.

'And who told *her*?' Kenda asked thoughtfully.

'Not me,' he said softly.

'I know that!'

'Do you? Well, well, we are making progress. But it's pretty common knowledge,' he pointed out almost gently. 'And he *did* die.'

'I know he died, but not because of anything *I* did.'

'Tell me.'

'No.'

'You prefer people to think you're some wicked little tramp?'

'I *am* a wicked little tramp. You said so.'

'No, I didn't,' he contradicted, a little lick of humour in his eyes.

'Implied it. And why can't you argue properly?' she demanded aggrievedly. 'You could make a person violent!'

'You *are* violent. Look what you did to Richard's clothes.'

'That wasn't violent. That was deserved.' Without waiting for any further comment, she pushed back into his bedroom and through to her own temporary accommodation. Don't become bitter, she warned herself. And she didn't care what people thought. *She* knew she hadn't done anything. But she was definitely going to sue Richard, she promised herself.

Surprisingly, she slept, and there were no thoughts of Richard, or Carrick, to trouble her dreams. When she woke, it was to find Carrick's bedroom empty, his bed made with military precision, a fire burning in the lounge and coffee percolating on the table by the window. Pouring herself a cup, she stared out. 'It's stopped raining,' she stated softly and in some surprise.

'Yes,' Carrick agreed as he entered through the outer door carrying logs for the fire. 'It doesn't *always* rain in Devon.'

'Just seems like it?' She smiled as she turned to look at him. Dressed in a dark grey T-shirt, loose, comfortable trousers tucked into soft leather boots, he looked fresh, disgustingly healthy, businesslike— and that little lick of pain spiralled low in her tummy. Quickly returning her gaze to the window, in case he should see something in her eyes, she stared blindly out.

'It's October. Don't you have rain in London in October? And it's seven-thirty,' he informed her.

'I know. I'll be on time.'

He nodded, bent to stack the logs tidily, dusted off his hands and walked out.

Cursing herself for a fool, she carried her coffee into the bedroom and laid out clean jeans and a loose sweater before going into the bathroom to shower.

Not bothering with make-up, she ran lightly down to the kitchen, made herself some toast, and entered the hall at exactly eight o'clock. The others were already there, a mixed bunch with ages ranging from early twenties, like David, to late thirties. Not all of them looked alert.

Carrick was standing on the hearth, his back to the fire, and was looking rather distastefully at the remains of the group's breakfast still lying on the hall table. 'Schedule,' he announced, slapping a piece of paper down beside the still warm coffee-pot. 'Read it, obey it. The knights will go with

Kenda to be fitted out and advised. The rest of you put on the padded jackets I've left by the door and come with me.'

One smart alec saluted. Carrick wasn't amused. 'You wish to learn, I will teach you. If you don't, leave. Now,' he added softly, 'you have four days to try and master skills that take years to perfect. You will be worked hard,' he warned. 'You knew that when you accepted. If you aren't prepared to work, then I'm wasting my time—and I don't have time to waste. And you will *not* flirt with Kenda.'

There were a couple of sniggers, which were frowned into silence, and a wry look from Kenda.

'Ellen,' he continued shortly, 'remember what I told you. Either observe from a window or learn from Kenda, but stay away from the practice ground.'

'I don't know why you have to be so inflexible. It surely can't hurt to teach a woman. Just because—'

He cut her short. 'No argument, no discussion. I don't teach women. The subject is now closed. You wish to learn about battle plans, procedure, the theory, go with Kenda and she will teach you.'

Gee, thanks, Kenda thought.

'If you say so,' Ellen stated pithily.

'I do say so.' Stepping down from the hearth, he walked out towards the courtyard. There was a mad scramble to follow him.

Extraordinarily glad that *she* wasn't about to learn warfare, Kenda set off for the workroom.

'Isn't Richard Marsh coming?' David asked when she'd settled them all in and was showing them how to dress.

'No,' she said shortly. 'Right. Mail hauberk, or tunic, with a built-in coif and long sleeves, together with mail hosen. The quilted cap goes *under* the coif.'

'I'll never be able to fight wearing all this!' one of them complained.

'Yes, you will; that's why you're here—to learn.'

'Well, why can't I learn in jeans and jumper and *then* get dressed up like an oven-ready turkey?'

'Because,' she explained patiently, 'if you start off in modern dress, by the time you do wear the mail, you will have to unlearn all you've been taught so far. Swords will get caught in the armour, in other people's armour, you'll have to learn how to walk differently, move differently...'

'OK, point taken.'

'Thank you,' she said drily. 'We do know what we're doing, and this armour is a hell of a lot lighter than what would have been worn. Right, headgear,' she continued. 'And just to show you that I'm not completely heartless I'll let you wear the nasal helmet instead of the helm; at least this way you'll be able to see other than only to the front. Carrick will show you how to wear your sword-belt. Gauntlets—'

'They don't have fingers!'

'No, fingered gauntlets didn't come in until the end of the century. Sorry.'

'And what's this horrendous-looking thing?'

'Collar. Think yourself lucky I didn't insist on steel plates being inserted. It's to protect your neck against sword thrusts and it laces at the front. Worn *over* your mail.

'And remember, mail protects against sword cuts but a heavy blow from a mace or axe might break bones inside, or a strong thrust from a pointed weapon might force the rings apart. I'm not trying to tell you how to act, but if, in the heat of battle, you got walloped with an axe, in all likelihood you would have been felled. When you've progressed to fighting on horseback I'll show you how to fit the leg protectors.' Glancing at her watch, she grinned. 'Go on, off you go; Carrick will be waiting. And send up the infantry, will you?'

With a little smile, she turned—and found Ellen missing. Where the hell had she gone? Hopefully not out to the practice ground, because if she had Kenda just *knew* who was going to get the blame!

When the infantrymen came up, she issued them with shorter length hauberks with elbow-length sleeves and no coif. 'You can wear either a kettle hat, skullcap, or no headgear at all. Some did, some didn't, so I'll leave it up to you. And thank your lucky stars you don't have to wear the mail hose. Go on, off you go; go and practise piking someone.'

Clearing away, she left her books and notes on the battle in case any of them wanted to look something up, and decided to go and have some lunch. She would give her talks on the battle when it got dark and Carrick could no longer teach outside.

She ate with Martin in the kitchen; Carrick presumably ate on the hoof, so to speak. She could hear sundry shouts and curses from outside, and decided to watch for a while from the safety of one of the upper windows.

Elbows on the sill, she smiled. The knights looked hot, bothered, and extraordinarily clumsy. Carrick

looked—supple and extremely graceful as he
showed them—probably for the fortieth time—the
moves they were supposed to be making.

Further over, she could just make out the targets.
One had several arrows sticking in it, the others
none, and then she saw Ellen wander across to
where the knights were practising—and get shouted
at by Carrick. He said something to the men then
firmly escorted Ellen back to the castle and out of
her sight.

Deciding to go down to the workroom and begin
on her mock-up of a neolithic hill village for the
following week, she met Carrick on his way up. He
looked furious.

'Trouble?'

'That *bloody* woman!' he exploded. 'Is she trying
to get herself killed? I told you to keep an eye on
her!'

'No, you didn't.'

Glaring at her, he sighed. 'No, I didn't,' he
agreed. 'Sorry. I just wish she would do as she's
damn well told.'

'She wants to be important,' Kenda said softly.

'Then she should go and save whales!'

'What a pity it's too late for suffragettes.'

'And I am not in the mood for *your* brand of
humour.'

'Then grow a thicker skin. And was it *entirely*
necessary to tell them not to flirt with me?' she
queried lightly.

'Yes, I—'

'Carrick?' Ellen demanded shrilly from somewhere below, and he closed his eyes in defeat.

'She obviously still fancies you,' she quipped.

'The way you fancy me?' he asked derisively.

'I don't fancy you,' she denied automatically with a little thrill of shock. 'I dislike you.'

'The way you disliked Peter? And James? And Neville?'

'I don't know anyone called Neville.'

'What a surprise!'

'Look, will you stop this? You want a row, go and row with Ellen!'

'No, she's not nearly so much fun! There's something about that woman that—'

'Is behind you,' Kenda said softly.

'What?'

With a little indication of her head, a little twitch to her lips, she added, 'She's brought her bow.'

'She hasn't got a bow.'

'She has now.'

'Has she?' Staring down into her exquisite face, at eyes that held mockery, at a mouth that promised, and probably gave, he carefully removed a piece of cotton that was clinging to one of her curls.

In flat shoes, she had to look up slightly, and, feeling suddenly breathless, not quite liking the look in his dark grey eyes, she flattened herself against the wall in an involuntary movement that brought a rather mirthless smile to his face.

'Nice to know someone's afraid of me.'

'I'm not afraid of you, and hadn't you better go and take that bow away from her?'

'No.' Sounding unemotional, distant, he swiftly dipped his head, and captured her mouth in a devastating kiss that robbed her of thought. He moved his mouth on hers with a skill and mastery that left her weak and yearning, unable to fight, unable to protest, because, in truth, it was what she *wanted*, and for one blissful moment she gave in to temptation, kissed him back—and it was he who drew away, put a small distance between them.

He stared at her, and she stared back, her breathing erratic.

'What did you do that for?' she demanded raggedly.

'Shock tactics?'

'Then I suggest you keep your tactics to yourself.' But her words were weak, unmeant. She wanted him back in her arms.

'Don't like a taste of your own medicine?'

'You don't know what my medicine is like.'

'No, but I've guessed,' he said quietly. 'Constantly.'

'What?' Not understanding any of this—not the look in his grey eyes, nor the tension in his hard body—for once in her life, she was unsure of what response was required. If any. It didn't feel like the tension of anger, or even dislike—and his breathing was as ragged as hers.

'More?' he taunted.

'No,' she said, meaning yes. 'And if this little demonstration is to dissuade Ellen from pursuing you I suggest you find another deterrent.'

'But I like this one.' Gathering her against him, he kissed her again. But not like before, not *at all* like before, and so there wasn't even a token struggle. There was a sweetness to it, a gentleness, a warmth, and as his hands moved over her with stunning assurance she weakly gave in to feelings she had only ever dreamed about, kissed him back with all the passion she was capable of until she felt mindless—and needed so much more.

He was experienced and expert, exciting, and it felt so—right, as though they had been made for each other. They fitted exactly, curve to curve, the right height, the right everything, and warmth flowed through her, pleasure flowed through her—and they kissed for a very long time.

Ellen was forgotten, the practice sessions were forgotten as they continued to exchange kisses, ignite passion. She slid her palms to frame his face, touched his neat ears, the hair at his nape, her movements eager, uncontrolled, avid, until a door slammed somewhere to disturb them.

They drew back, stared at each other, both breathing heavily. Both aroused.

'You want me,' she stated thickly, because surprise had robbed her of common sense.

'Yes,' he agreed. 'And don't I just *hate* myself for wanting a woman with such suspect morals?'

'What?' she whispered in distress. He hadn't kissed her because he'd realised he'd been wrong about her. He had not kissed her out of liking, or affection, or promise—and he could not have caused more pain if he had slapped her. Tawny eyes wide, so much hurt in them, she exclaimed stupidly, 'I *liked* you!'

'Well, don't like me now,' he ordered softly. 'I prefer my clothing unshredded.' Releasing her, he indicated for her to go.

Unable to think of anything to say, feeling dazed and disbelieving, she turned to walk along the corridor. Forced herself not to run. Reaching the intersection, she halted, looked back. He was standing where she had left him, watching her.

'*Why?*' she demanded. 'And if you hate me so much, why did you allow me to come?'

'I was bored,' he said simply. 'I thought you might relieve it.' Sketching an insulting salute, he walked away.

Bored? *Bored?* Not knowing where she was going, why she was going, she walked down to the kitchen, gave a half-laugh that was incredibly filled with pain. He'd invited her out of *boredom*? He'd kissed her because he could not help himself—as men often wanted to kiss her, as though she were an object, not a person at all? An adventure, he'd said to Martin. Was that what he'd meant? And haven't you been goading him, she asked herself honestly, because you wanted an adventure of your own? Because you *wanted* him to kiss you? But wanting and inviting insult were two very different things. She couldn't even afford to leave. Dammit, she wasn't going to leave. She wouldn't give him the satisfaction!

Pushing open the kitchen door, she saw Martin standing at the stove. He began to smile, then frowned.

'Is something wrong?'

'Yes,' she agreed tautly. 'I just made a very big mistake.' A monumental mistake. She had allowed her guard to slip, invited derision.

'Oh, dear. Anything I can do?'

'What? Oh, no. No!' Giving him a distracted smile, she accepted the tea he put into her hands. 'Thanks.'

'Can it be rectified?'

'I don't know. Probably not.'

'Sorry?'

'Hmm? Oh, nothing. Take no notice.' Did he hate himself? Yes, because a man like that needed to be in control, and if his feelings didn't obey his mind he *would* hate himself. And her, presumably. Yet despite it all she wanted to be back in his arms, wanted to feel his mouth moving on hers, over and over and over again. She wanted—fulfilment, because no one had ever made her feel the way he could make her feel just by being. Startled, she examined the statement and found it true. He made her feel—alive.

She didn't have commitments; she was never in one place long enough to make them. She'd had two relationships in her twenty-eight years, only one intimate, despite what anyone else might think, and not many friends. She had a passionate interest in history—and not much else, she suddenly realised. And she'd just been shaken to her roots by a man who disliked and despised her.

'I'm twenty-eight,' she announced to a somewhat bemused Martin.

'Are you?' he asked in some bewilderment. 'Is that a problem?'

'Yes. No. Have you ever been married, Martin?'

'No. Never found anyone that was right, I suppose.' Coming to sit opposite her, hands round his mug, he continued, 'With Carrick's father and his wife as role models, I didn't want to settle for anything less than they had. Adored each other, they did. Lived for each other, and when he died she was like a little lost soul. A ghost. I've never met anyone that would make me want to get up in the morning, let alone devote the rest of my life to her. And so I stayed single.'

'Like Carrick.'

'I suppose. You didn't want to marry?' he asked.

'I don't know. Sorry, I'm not making much sense, am I?'

'No.'

Heaving a big sigh, she sipped her cooling tea.

'The pilot's OK, by the way,' Martin murmured. 'The hospital just rang.'

'Oh, good.' But thinking of the pilot brought back memories of a naked back, of the man who'd just kissed her. In an effort to distract herself, she announced, 'I need some plasticine.'

'Plasticine?'

'Yes, or modelling clay. I'm making a model of Mai-Dun. For next week,' she explained when he looked blank. 'It was a neolithic hill village near Dorchester. Sacked by the Romans in AD 44.'

'Oh, right. Combe Martin has a craft shop.'

With an absent nod, she finished her tea. 'I'll drive in now. Thanks.'

Getting to her feet, she wandered out and upstairs to collect her coat and car keys. Coming down the stairs to the first landing, she heard David's voice and walked along the corridor to see what he was up to. She felt—displaced.

Peering into the open door of the armoury, she saw Carrick seated at the bench, filing a wooden sword. David was just lifting down the longbow from the wall. He didn't tell *him* not to touch it. 'Why can't we use these?'

'Because your lot could never pull them,' Carrick answered absently. 'It's a hundred and twenty pounds pull weight.'

David attempted it and could only manage a few inches.

'A good archer could fire ten arrows a minute and hit a target up to three hundred yards, which was why they were so very effective in battle. The French had few disciplined infantry because they considered battle to be the exclusive and honourable business of aristocratic armoured cavalry.'

'They despised archers as their social inferiors,' Kenda put in quietly from the doorway, her eyes on Carrick's back, 'and for many years didn't bother to develop tactics to defeat them. Again and again, large French armies of knights and men-at-arms were slaughtered by smaller English armies in which bowmen outnumbered knights by three or four to one.'

'No wonder Ellen wanted to be one!' David exclaimed. 'Can you pull it?' he asked Carrick as he replaced it on the wall.

'Yes. Here,' he added as he tossed him the sword he'd been filing. 'Try not to trip over it again.'

'Right.' Fumbling the catch, David grinned at Kenda. 'Were you looking for me?'

'No,' she said, her eyes still fixed on Carrick, 'I was just thinking of popping into Combe Martin if nobody needs me for a bit.'

'I will always need you,' he announced dramatically, 'but I have to practise. See you later.' With a wink, he walked off.

Wanting to move, unable to find the will-power, Kenda stayed where she was, and an eternity later Carrick turned to look at her, and she shivered.

'Another scalp?' he asked quietly.

'No,' she denied. 'I'm just going into Combe Martin. I need some modelling clay.'

He didn't answer, didn't move; neither did she. Then slowly, so very slowly, he put down the file he'd been using and got to his feet. Kenda fled.

'Kenda?' he called after her quietly.

'No,' she said inaudibly.

'Kenda!'

Halting, she looked reluctantly back, watched as he meticulously locked the armoury door, put the keys in his pocket, his eyes never once leaving hers. 'No,' she repeated tonelessly. *No.* Hurrying on and down the stairs, she went out to her car.

Driving almost blindly along winding, tree-lined roads, then up onto the main route towards Ilfracombe, she thought about it again and again. A kiss to destroy the mind. How could she be so affected by a kiss from a man who despised her?

Automatically following the road signs, she drove down into the small town, found a parking space by the sea wall, and then just sat and stared at an angry sea, at wheeling seagulls, a small, deserted beach. She wanted him, she thought bleakly, on any terms at all. And that was crazy. With a big sigh, she climbed from the car, locked it, and began to wander round the town in search of the craft shop.

She eventually found what she wanted, used most of what little money she had left, and returned reluctantly to the castle. Parking tidily, mind still on

Carrick, she climbed out, parcel clutched in her hand, and walked across the cobbled yard. Nick, one of the 'pikemen', came hurrying out of the side-gate, a grimace on his young face, and she gave him an absent smile.

'Broke me pike!' he exclaimed humorously. 'Carrick's sent me to get another one.'

Pushing open the heavy outer door, she turned to answer him—and a crossbow bolt thudded into her, pinning her to the wood.

CHAPTER FOUR

SHOCK held Kenda rigid, and the sudden silence was deafening. Then Ellen screamed, dropped the crossbow—and Carrick came running. He stared briefly at the bolt that was quivering a fraction of an inch from Kenda's jaw, moved his eyes to hers, and then instructed the shocked and immobile actor. 'Hold her; don't let her move. And don't touch the bolt.'

Snatching the keys from his hand, he leaped for the stairs, took them two at a time and returned moments later, carrying some cutters.

'Keep as still as you can,' he ordered Kenda grimly as the young man held her in place. Cutting the shaft as close to her jacket as he could, Carrick carefully eased the cutters behind her and cut the bolt where it entered the door. She sagged, and it was he who caught her, held her against him. Numb, incapable of speech, she just stared at him, eyes too big, too wide.

'It's all right,' he said softly, and there was such comfort and assurance in his eyes that she accepted his words without question.

Handing the cutters to Nick, he said quietly, and with such menace that Kenda flinched, 'Get that woman out of here. I don't care how you do it, I don't care where you take her, but I want her gone. Understand?'

'Yes,' Nick promised, his voice shaking. 'How bad is it?'

'I don't know.'

'It could have killed her. If she hadn't turned back to speak to me, it would have...'

'Yes,' Carrick agreed grimly. Easing Kenda across to his other side, so that he could hold her without hurting her injured shoulder, he saw that the others had all come running at the sound of Ellen's scream. 'Go back to your practising—*only* the moves I showed you. If there's a problem ask Jason or Martin to help.'

'It was an accident!' Ellen pleaded, and Carrick stared at her.

'I hope it was,' he stated coldly. 'If I thought it was anything else, you wouldn't be leaving.' Turning back to Kenda, he asked, 'Can you ease your good arm from your jacket?'

She swallowed, nodded, and, her shocked eyes still fixed widely on his face, shrugged her arm free. 'I don't think—'

'Shh.'

His face still with concentration, he eased her coat round her back, gently lifted the collar away from her neck, carefully probed, and explained comfortingly, 'It's gone through your coat and sweater, gouged a groove in your neck, but it's not embedded in your flesh.'

She shivered, nodded.

'A fraction lower...' Nick began, and Carrick stared him into silence.

'I gave you an order.'

He let out a shuddery sigh and moved away.

'Come on.' One arm round her, Carrick led Kenda up to his quarters, eased her coat completely off and sat her on one of the long sofas. Tossing the coat over one of the chairs, he went to get the medicine box from the bathroom.

'I need to cut your sweater,' he said quietly.

She nodded, fixed her gaze on the fire as he gently cut away the shoulder seam of her jumper and examined the cut. 'Are your tetanus injections up to date?'

'Yes,' she whispered.

'This might sting.'

She nodded again, braced herself, sucked in a little breath as he carefully cleaned the wound and then taped a dressing over it. 'It will probably leave a small scar.'

'Doesn't matter.' Swallowing to clear what felt like an obstruction in her throat, she asked shakily, 'What was she doing with a crossbow in the hall?'

'I don't know,' he said grimly. 'Blatantly stupid defiance because I took the bow away from her, no doubt.'

'Did you? Take it away, I mean?'

'Yes.' Walking across to the bar, he poured her a generous measure of brandy. 'Here, drink this.'

Taking the glass, she said stupidly, 'You keep giving me brandy.'

'Yes. Drink it; you're as white as a sheet. I'll get Martin to bring you up some tea.' Walking away, he returned seconds later with a woollen shawl, instructed her to lean forward, then gently draped it round her shoulders. 'Stay here. Keep warm. You're in shock.'

And wasn't that the truth? 'Where are you going?'

'To interrogate Ellen.' His face cold and hard, he left.

With her shoulder throbbing, feeling sick and shaken, she sipped her brandy, continued to stare into the fire, felt a lone tear trickle down her cheek, and impatiently wiped it away. It had been an accident, and it could have been worse. If she hadn't turned back to speak to young Nick, it would have gone through her jaw.

Finishing her brandy, she laid her head on the cushioned arm of the sofa, kicked off her shoes and lifted her feet up. Staring at the fire, her shocked mind still trying to comprehend what had happened, astonishingly she fell asleep. She didn't know what woke her—a small sound, a log settling in the grate, maybe—but it was enough to bring her out of sleep.

Opening her eyes a fraction, she stared at Carrick, who was lounging on the sofa opposite. He looked—well, sadly self-mocking was the nearest she could come to describing it. Absurd, because why would he look like that? Angry, maybe, grim, but self-mocking?

He had such a strong face, and a wickedly attractive mouth. A mouth that had touched hers. She could almost still feel the hard imprint of it, still feel the warmth of his body, and she gave a little shiver. A very male animal. So few men had the presence, the magnetic quality that Carrick exuded. And all for what? she wondered bleakly. A reputation she had gained through no fault of her own preceded her wherever she went. And because men found her attractive it was believed.

As though aware of being watched, he raised his eyes, and she looked quickly away, her heart jerking. The table-lamps were lit, the curtains drawn across the window, giving the room an intimacy that was troubling. A pot of tea sat on the coffee-table between the couches, along with a plate of sandwiches.

'Martin thought you might be hungry,' he said quietly. 'How do you feel?'

'I'm all right. What time is it?'

'Half-six, and in the space of two days,' he continued musingly, 'we've had a plane crash, a flood, a shooting. What else is in store for us, I wonder?'

Sex? 'Nothing.' Avoiding his eyes, she sat up, pushed a cushion behind her, eased her sore shoulder into a more comfortable position. 'Has Ellen gone?'

'Yes.'

Feeling awkward, constrained, she watched him get to his feet and walk to stand in front of the fire. She didn't want him standing. Standing, he intimidated her.

Moving with a grace that most men would envy, he faced her and stared at her almost assessingly. 'You should come with a government health warning,' he said quietly.

'You think I was the catalyst?'

'I didn't mean the accidents; I meant the effect you have on men.'

'I haven't caused trouble with the trainees,' she defended herself as she leaned forward and poured herself a cup of tea.

'No,' he agreed, his voice soft, reflective. 'Only the tutor.'

Startled, she flicked her eyes up to his, looked quickly away, and reached for a sandwich she didn't want. 'And that's my fault, is it—that you find me attractive?'

'Yes. And do you find me attractive in return?'

'No,' she lied quickly, and found that her heart was beating too fast, her hands shaking.

'David?'

'No.'

'Nick?'

'No.'

'Tell me what happened at the museum.'

'You mean you don't *know*?' she asked in sarcastic disbelief as she fought to keep her emotions on an even keel.

'I've heard rumour, innuendo, and pocket psychologists giving their interpretations, but do I *know*? No.'

'Well, you know what they say—ignorance is bliss.'

'Don't be flippant.'

'I feel flippant. I've just had a narrow escape from death.' Returning the sandwich to the plate, she made a dismissive little gesture that could have meant anything or nothing, and continued to keep her eyes very firmly away from him.

'And Richard?'

'I don't want to talk about Richard either. And I have to go and give my talk on the Battle of Crécy.'

'It's been cancelled.'

'I don't want it cancelled,' she said shakily. 'I'm quite capable of giving a talk.'

'No, you aren't, and it's still cancelled.'

'Then I'll move back to my old room.'

'The men are using it.'

'Then I'll use Ellen's!' she bit out, aggravated beyond endurance. 'Don't let me keep you; I'm sure you have lots of things to do. I don't need a babysitter.'

'No,' he agreed quietly. 'Just a minder.'

Finishing her tea, she got to her feet, swayed, wanted to hit something. Or someone. 'I'm all right,' she snapped when he reached out to steady her. 'I don't want you touching me!'

'No,' he agreed softly. 'It tends to lead to other things, doesn't it?'

Off balance, feeling tearful, avoiding his eyes, she said hastily, 'I'll go and get my things.'

He merely nodded, waited until she'd reached the far side of the lounge before saying, 'I owe you an apology.'

Swinging round, she said flatly, 'I don't want your apology.'

He gave a faint, rueful smile. 'You have it nevertheless. That was why I called after you, before you went into the village.'

'A precautionary measure in case I decide to shred your clothes?' she asked derisively. 'You don't need to worry; you aren't nearly worth the effort!'

Hurrying through his bedroom and into the dressing room, tears blurring her vision, she slammed the door. She'd been insulted, nearly killed... How *could* she still want a man who hated her?

Bundling up her things, muscles clenched for another confrontation, she stalked out—to find that he'd gone. Shaking, as much from confronting Carrick as from reaction to the accident, she walked along to the room recently vacated by Ellen and dumped everything on the bed. Sinking down beside her belongings, she dragged a deep breath into her lungs and fought to remain calm, steady. Hearing a small movement, she snapped her head up defensively, then relaxed when she saw Martin hovering in the doorway, a bundle of linen in his arms.

'Don't be nice to me,' she ordered thickly. 'I'll grizzle.'

'Wouldn't dream of it,' he said, but his voice was somewhat fainter than usual, and the expression in his eyes sympathetic. 'But you look like a lady who needs a big hug.'

With an involuntary sniff, a shaky little sigh, she managed a smile. 'Yeah.'

'Carrick said you were moving rooms. I came to change the sheets.' Dropping them on the bed, he touched her arm. 'Come on.'

Surprised, she got to her feet. 'Where are we going?'

'To my rooms. The men will be up shortly to shower, change, enquire—make a lot of noise. You need a bit of peace and quiet.' Leading her along the corridor, he pushed open his own door, ushered her into a lounge. Smaller than Carrick's, it was nevertheless cosy, comfortable. Indicating for her to sit, he added, 'I'll make you some tea, then you can do as you please. Rest, read, have a little sleep.'

Grateful, for once, at having someone take charge of her, she did as she was told, and when he brought her up a meal a few hours later she managed to eat most of it. They spent the rest of the evening playing

Scrabble and there was no mention of the accident,
or of Carrick.

The rest of the week was so busy that there was
no chance of any more confrontations—for which
she was profoundly thankful, she told herself—and
apart from the absence of Ellen and the hole in the
outer door where the bolt had struck there was
nothing to show that any drama had ever taken
place. There had been commiserations and concern
the first day, but after that it had all seemed
forgotten.

Carrick pushed his trainees from dawn till dusk,
and then Kenda took over, cramming as much information into them as was possible. Meals were
taken together and were useful for discussion,
further learning, and they were usually still all
talking when she went up to bed. She carried out
her duties meticulously, and Carrick looked either
thoughtful or hatefully amused. Why? He'd been
angry when he'd kissed her, had hated her after-
wards, and now he was amused?

Friday morning, they all left, and Kenda made a
firm resolve to go out, look at countryside and villages—anything to be away from the castle for a
few hours. She'd probably have to beg some money
off Martin for petrol, she thought miserably; certainly she didn't intend to ask Carrick for an advance on her salary. If Richard hadn't proved such
a traitor...

It was no good thinking like that, and she still
hadn't contacted a lawyer. Perhaps she could find
one in Combe Martin or Minehead—except she

didn't have any money to pay one. You had to pay
for a consultation, didn't you?

Walking along the top corridor, coat over her
arm, car keys in her hand, as she neared Carrick's
quarters she heard voices—Carrick's, Martin's, and
someone else's. Cursing her choice of route, before
she could retreat she heard her name mentioned,
and, curious, halted to listen.

'And is Miss McKinley intending to countersue?'

With a little frown, not thinking, she walked to
stand in the open doorway and demanded, 'Countersue what?'

'Not what, who,' Carrick corrected her. 'Eaves-
dropping?' he asked silkily.

'No. I heard my name mentioned.'

'Then you'd best come in. Ian Furber, my solicitor.' He introduced the other man. 'He wants to
know if you are intending to countersue Ellen.'

'*Counter*sue? Why? Is she suing me?'

'No. Me. For stress caused by my negligence.'
He still looked hatefully amused.

'Negligence?' Kenda exclaimed in astonishment.

'Yes.'

'He allegedly left the armoury unlocked and the
crossbow loaded on the bench—an open invitation
for mayhem,' Ian explained as he watched her curiously. There was no mistaking the appreciation
in his eyes.

Ignoring it, as she always tried to ignore men's
admiration, she stared from one to the other, then
shook her head. 'No.'

'No?'

'No,' she repeated. 'Whatever else he is or does,
that is one thing he would *not* do. He *always* locks

the armoury door, as he did that day. And that crossbow was locked in its case before I went to Combe Martin.'

'Are you sure?'

'Yes.'

Turning to Carrick, he asked, 'And can it be proved that you didn't leave the practice yard that afternoon before Miss McKinley returned and was subsequently shot?'

'Yes,' Carrick confirmed, his eyes on Kenda. Laughter was dancing in their depths, and she wanted to go and smack him.

'And would you be willing to swear on oath,' he asked Kenda, 'that the room was locked before you went to the town?'

'Yes.'

'How can you be so sure?'

'Because I watched him lock it!'

'He didn't leave the keys in the door?'

'No, he put them in his pocket.'

'You're certain?'

'Of course I'm certain! They were pressing into my groin when he assaulted me!'

'*Assaulted* you?' he exclaimed in astonished disbelief.

'Yes.'

'Kissed her,' Carrick argued laconically.

'Against my will—which constitutes assault.'

'You wish to sue?' Carrick asked drily.

'No, with my track record, you would argue it was provoked,' she retorted. 'And stop laughing,' she told Martin crossly. He tried to straighten his face and she returned her attention to the solicitor. '*Why* is she suing?'

'Hell hath no fury?' he offered, and blinked in surprise when Kenda snorted and Carrick chuckled. Composing himself, he asked Carrick, 'Was the armoury door locked when you went for the cutters after Miss McKinley was shot?'

'Yes. I took the keys from Nick, one of the trainees.'

'He had them all the time you were in the practice yard?'

'No, they were in my jerkin, which was hanging up by the tack room.'

'So Miss Marks could have taken them, appropriated the crossbow, and then returned them without your knowledge?'

'Yes.'

'And why, in your opinion, did she want the crossbow?'

'Presumably because I refused to teach her the longbow. She was trying to prove a point. That women are equally proficient in firing a lethal weapon.'

'And was that in doubt?'

'No. I was merely reluctant to teach her.' Lounging against the back of the sofa, he shoved his hands into his pockets and continued to watch Kenda.

'It wasn't reluctance,' Kenda put in. 'It was a flat refusal. And women *are* capable. He was just being vindictive.'

Carrick gave a small, hateful smile. 'I know women are capable—I've seen it demonstrated time and time again—and I was not being vindictive; I merely have a rule that I don't teach them. Women are unpredictable, and a distraction. And don't snort, Kenda; it isn't attractive.

'When I'm training,' he resumed, presumably for the solicitor's benefit—she certainly didn't think it was for hers. 'I need all my attention focused on what I'm doing. Even if she hadn't been here before, caused trouble before, I still wouldn't have taught her. Any more than I teach people who make individual enquiries.

'I have a responsibility to ensure that these skills don't fall into the wrong hands, that they are used only for films, television series, reputable groups. I do not teach thugs to stab old ladies; I do not teach gangs to stage their own private wars. And I do not,' he repeated provokingly, 'teach women, who, in my opinion, are far more dangerous than men.'

'We are,' Kenda told him kindly.

'Yes,' Ian agreed, a rather fascinated light in his eyes as he watched them spur. 'And so, in effect, any stress she subsequently suffered following the accident was caused solely by herself, by her own refusal to obey your rules.'

'Yes,' Carrick agreed, still watching Kenda.

'And you don't wish to sue her for your injury, Miss McKinley?'

'No,' she said, refusing to look away from Carrick. 'It was an accident.'

'Very well. Leave it with me.'

Carrick straightened, shook hands with him, and Kenda moved inside the door to let him pass. Martin gave her a humorous look and followed the solicitor in order to show him out.

'He should take silk,' she grumbled crossly. 'He'd make a good prosec—' Eyes suddenly wide, she made an abrupt move towards the door, intending to go after him.

Carrick moved more swiftly than she would have believed possible and got there first. He closed the door and stood with his back against it.

'Let me out.'

'No.'

'I need to speak with the solicitor.'

'Why?'

Stamping her foot, she exclaimed crossly, 'Never mind why! Just let me out!'

'No. You lied,' he reproved her softly. 'I didn't kiss you after I'd locked the door.'

'You shouldn't have kissed me at all!'

'I *know* that!'

'So?'

'So why did you say so?'

Not wishing to discuss the kiss, or anything pertaining to it, she shrugged into her jacket and faced him defiantly. 'Move away from the door.'

'No. You could have caused me a lot of trouble.'

'And don't I just wish I had!' she declared mutinously. 'Carrick, I need to speak with Mr Furber!'

'You could have kept quiet,' he continued, unmoved. 'Why didn't you?'

'Because I'm not vindictive!' she snapped.

'Tell me about Peter Dawson.'

'No.'

'*Tell* me!'

'Why? So you can justify your hatred?' Glaring at him, hating him, wanting him, she burst out, 'The very first time I saw you, I *liked* you! I imagined such *glories*! And don't look so astonished,' she reproved him irritably. 'You must know what effect you have on women!'

'Much the same as you have on men?' he asked lightly. 'I liked you too, *despite* all the rumours I'd heard. Hope springs eternal, doesn't it? Or stupidity. Like Peter. Who killed himself—'

'Died,' she interrupted flatly.

'All right, died,' he agreed, with a little dip of his head. 'I don't know you, only your face, how you make me feel—and a lot of other men,' he tacked on with self-deprecation. 'People don't generally lie for no reason, and, even allowing for exaggeration, there must be some truth to the accusations, because it wasn't only Peter, was it? There was James Lincoln.'

'I *told* you about James. And if we must discuss this, can we discuss it later? I need to see the solicitor!'

'He'll be long gone. Why do you need to see him?'

'Oh, for pity's sake!' she exploded, turning away in disgust.

'Pity certainly seems to come into it somewhere,' he agreed. 'Tell me about Neville.'

'I don't know anyone named Neville.'

'He knows you. Said you'd been lovers. That you dumped him for someone else. ''A butterfly with a low attention span for men,'' he said. You accused me of not liking women, but you don't like men, do you?'

'I've had good reason not to,' she said bitterly.

'And that's why you are like you are?'

'No!' Incensed, she swung round to deny it. 'I'm *not* like everyone says I am! My God, men see a pretty face, a body that's adequate—'

'Exquisite,' he corrected her.

'All right,' she snapped, 'exquisite! And because I won't go out with them, don't want their damned compliments, they spread stories about me, boast that they've slept with me! Now, is that rational? You're a man—is that rational? I don't make up stories about men! Why the hell should they make up stories about me? They've *always* done so! Ever since I—developed! My father was a bully and a liar. Expected signs of affection I wasn't prepared to give! *Father*,' she spat. 'Foster-father!'

'You were fostered?' he asked in surprise.

'Why so astonished?' she demanded. 'People are.'

'Yes. Sorry.'

'I don't know who I am!' she burst out. 'I can't say, Oh, I'm like my father or mother. I get my temper from Aunt Alice or Uncle Fred. Whose genes made me the person I am?' she asked rhetorically. 'Were they responsible for my aggression? Or is that the result of frustration, anger? I don't know, you see,' she announced flatly. 'I don't have a yardstick, a role model.'

'And that excuses your behaviour?'

'Of course it doesn't!' she denied crossly. 'But I'm not immoral—amoral—oh, you know what I mean!'

'Yes. Fostered from how old?'

'From birth. Not the same couple. I was—difficult,' she explained with a bleak smile. 'Got moved around a lot. And don't laugh or say you can understand why!'

'I wasn't going to. Did you try to find them— your real parents?'

'Yes, but I wasn't given up for adoption; there were no papers, no records. I was found in a telephone box in Kendal. McKinley was the name of the hospital they took me to. And it matters, Carrick. People will never know how much it matters.' Staring at him, her eyes holding a defiance that couldn't disguise her hurt, she demanded, 'And if you thought me so troublesome, took endless pains to find out I was troublesome, why did you agree that I could come? And don't tell me it was because you were bored!'

'I needed a historian.'

'You could have used Richard.'

'Richard doesn't have your knowledge of medieval Europe. What happened between you two?'

'Nothing. And I don't wish to *mention* Richard. I don't ever want to see him, talk about him, *think* about him!'

'Good. Then tell me about Peter Dawson.'

'Why?' she demanded bluntly.

'I don't like to misjudge people,' he said simply.

'And what happens if you find you've misjudged me? You'll *like* me?' she asked waspishly.

'Do you want me to?' He smiled, that damned amusement lurking in his eyes once more.

'No!'

He grinned. 'Tell me,' he persuaded her softly.

With a tired sigh, she turned away, went to stand at the window, as far away from him as she could get. What was the point? What really was the point?

'Peter was a fool,' she stated flatly. 'A middle-aged man hoping to recapture his lost youth or something. Or maybe he was going through the male menopause,' she added wearily. 'I don't know; who ever knows how people think? All I do know is that he wouldn't leave me alone. From the very first day at the museum, he—plagued me. Always in my office on one pretext or another, always in the corridor when I passed by, always in the canteen. Always making excuses to talk to me, consult me, praise me, compliment me.'

'You never should have smiled at him,' Carrick put in drily.

'I didn't smile at him, damn you!' she swung round to exclaim. 'Or only when we first met.'

'It's the first meeting that does it,' he agreed solemnly.

'Very funny. And then he began writing notes to me, phoning my flat, sending me flowers! And I wanted *none* of it!'

'Why didn't you claim sexual harassment?'

'Oh, don't be a fool! No one ever believes women don't invite it, expect it! You think I wanted my name dragged through the courts, only to be told it was my own fault? He looked harmless, bewildered, innocuous! A middle-aged man with a pot belly and a dutiful wife!'

'And yet he left her.'

'*She* left *him*! Because of his fantasising. She was the only one who didn't believe I was Delilah! She knew him, knew what he was like, and she said that even if everyone else wore blinkers she certainly didn't.' With a hollow laugh, Kenda added, 'She said that even if I did take him I'd soon bring him back! In fact, she said she wished I *would* take him!'

'Why didn't you complain to the director of the museum?'

'I did! He said it was my problem and to deal with it. He wouldn't even listen!' she exclaimed in remembered fury. 'Said Peter had been with them for thirty years and they'd *never* had any trouble until I joined them.'

'Then you should definitely have smiled at *him*!'

Goaded, near tears, she shouted, 'Shut up! He wouldn't believe I didn't want him! I tried *everything* to make him stop! I invented boyfriends, jealous lovers . . . I didn't know *what* to do! I even asked the police for advice. They said he hadn't committed an offence, and that until he did there was nothing they could do—and then the *policeman* asked me out! Stop laughing,' she yelled.

'Sorry,' he apologised as he tried to straighten his face, but he could apparently do nothing about the laughter in his eyes.

'It was affecting my work, my sleep . . .' Swinging back to the window, she stared blindly through the glass, her vision distorted by tears. Angrily brushing them away, she thumped her fists on the window-sill in frustration.

Moving up behind her, he put his hands on her shoulders, refused to have them shrugged away. Pulling her back against him, he slipped his arms around her, rested her head against his shoulder.

'Go on,' he prompted softly.

Her sigh deep, desperately trying to ignore the feelings the warmth of his body was generating, she continued quietly, 'It was still within my three-

month trial period, and I was told by the director
that if I couldn't keep my private life out of the
museum then I would have to leave. I told him that
because of Peter I didn't have a private life! He
called Peter in, and Peter looked crestfallen, apolo-
getic, told him that we were lovers, but it would be
all right because we would be getting married as
soon as he could get a divorce. No one believed my
denials—'

'Shouted denials?'

'Yes. Angry, frustrated, *screamed* denials. What
they *did* believe,' she went on grimly, 'was that we'd
had an affair and that I had thrown him over for
someone else.'

'One of your mythical lovers.'

'Yes. I shouldn't have lost my temper.'

'No.'

'I'm glad you find it amusing.'

'I don't,' he denied soberly. 'Go on.'

'Everyone overheard the shouting match that
ensued—staff, visitors—and everyone heard Peter
say that he would kill himself if I didn't go back
to him. How could I go back to him when I'd never
left him in the first place, never *wanted* him in the
first place? And Peter didn't shout—oh, no. He just
sobbed. It was awful,' she muttered in remembered
anguish.

'I'm sure it was.'

'And I don't believe he killed himself! I think he
had an accident because he wasn't paying attention
to his driving. So did the coroner, because *he*
brought in a verdict of accidental death! But the
museum still thought it best if I left,' she added
bitterly, 'so I did. I'm sorry he died,' she continued

more quietly. 'Despite all the trouble he caused me, I never wished for that.'

'I saw you,' he said quietly.

'What?' Distracted, confused, she craned round to look at him.

'I saw you,' he repeated. 'Oh, months ago, at Marling Studios. I asked who you were.'

'And got more information than you bargained for,' she said bitterly.

'Yes. It was just after Peter died.'

'I was looking for work. I didn't see you.'

'No. You left in a swirl of skirts and tossed hair. Glorious hair, like Old English treacle.'

'And you believed all that you were told,' she stated flatly.

'Not necessarily,' he denied.

'You didn't pursue the—acquaintance,' she muttered tartly.

'No, I had to return to Devon. My mother was dying,' he said sombrely.

Turning a stricken face towards him, she stared into his face and whispered, 'I'm sorry. Martin said you were very close.'

'Yes. And when she was stable, safe to leave for a short while, I came looking—because I couldn't stay away.'

Startled, not sure she believed him, she remained silent.

'But I couldn't find you.'

'I was busy,' she said evasively. 'Richard knew where I was.'

'Richard wasn't telling. And then Martin rang to say she had died. And because I felt guilty, anguished, because I should never have left her, I blamed you.'

'I didn't know,' she murmured.

'Of course you didn't. How could you?'

Not knowing how to answer, she shrugged. 'Anyway, that's what happened. And I don't care if you believe me or not.'

'Yes, you do,' he argued softly. 'And I do believe you. I also know how Peter felt. Utterly tormented.'

Turning, she looked up into his eyes. Tormented? He didn't *look* tormented, *act* tormented. 'And do you still hate yourself?' she mocked raggedly.

He didn't answer immediately, and she gave a scornful laugh. 'Even if you don't believe that Peter and I had an affair, you still think I encouraged him, don't you?'

'You encourage men just by being.'

'Then there's nothing more to say, is there?' she asked bleakly.

'Not to say, no.' Gathering her against him, he bent his head and captured her mouth with his own.

CHAPTER FIVE

'No!'

'Be quiet,' Carrick ordered softly and continued to taste her mouth. Kenda could feel the tension growing in him, and in herself, could feel his arousal—an arousal that was goading her, exciting her.

'You believed all that was said,' she argued desperately, knowing—*knowing*—that she wanted this above all else.

'What chance did I have of doing otherwise?' he asked absently as he moved his mouth to her cheekbone, her temple, his actions compulsive, restless. 'I didn't know you.'

'And now?'

He grunted, hugged her to him, his maleness a spur she was desperately trying to deny. 'I'm attracted to you.'

'So you said,' she agreed pithily, and he laughed.

'Probably about as much as you're attracted to me,' he continued, his voice soft, persuasive, throaty.

'No.'

'Yes. So what are we going to do about it?'

'By all means let's hold a *discussion* on it!'

'You want me to give you no choice?'

'No,' she retorted as the alarming possibilities flew through her head.

His movements rough, intense, he pushed his hands into her thick, curly hair, held it away from her exquisite face, stared deep into her stormy eyes. 'This isn't doing either of us any good,' he murmured mockingly.

'So what do you want to do?' she derided him sarcastically. 'Have an affair? Get it out of your system?'

'Yes,' he agreed simply as his mouth began an exploration of her jaw, and her stomach dropped.

'What?'

'Why not?'

'Why *not*? You really expect I will accommodate you after your insults?'

'Yes,' he said softly, 'because wanting me is eating away at your soul. You'll end up waspish.'

'I'm always waspish.'

'Because of me?'

'No. And don't keep kissing me! It's undermining!'

'It was meant to be.'

'Stop being absurd. We haven't known each other a week yet.'

'I know. Disgraceful, isn't it?'

'Carrick—'

'I saw you before...'

'That doesn't count.'

'Who's counting?' he murmured as he continued to blaze a fiery trail down her cheek.

Shoving him back a fraction, Kenda demanded, 'And is that why you let me come? Because you'd once seen me and...'

'Fancied you?' he mocked. 'Of course. I always did like a challenge. And is that your ruling? To know a man a week before you—'

'You dare!' she interrupted stormily. 'You just dare! And stop laughing! You've been *foul* to me since I've been here.'

'Yes. After seeing what you did to Richard's things, I was having second thoughts.'

'Then why have you changed your mind?'

Raising his head, he said simply, quietly, believingly, flatly, 'Because, dear lady, you are driving me insane. Stop talking, and, for the love of God, please, kiss me back. With passion.'

Eyes wide, she stared at him, stared at his mouth, wriggled uncomfortably because the need inside was growing so very hard to bear, closed her eyes, and exclaimed defeatedly, 'This is ridiculous! *And* you're aroused.'

He shook with laughter. 'So are you.'

'Hardly polite of you to point it out,' she grumbled, feeling stupid.

'You did.'

'You'll hurt me.'

'I'll try not to,' he soothed meekly.

'This is silly.'

'Yes.'

'We don't know each other.'

'No.'

'I don't *want* an affair with you.'

'Then don't have one.'

'Oh...' Shoving him away, she walked agitatedly across to the sofa, stood with her hands digging into its back. And she did want him—she'd wanted him from the first moment she'd met him, wanted him for the past extraordinary long, extraordinarily aggravating five days—and her body was already anticipating the delights to come. But you couldn't go to bed with someone you'd only known a few days! She wasn't *like* that!

'Battle over?' he asked softly from behind her.

'Do *you* go to bed with women you've only just met?' she demanded raggedly.

'No,' he denied gently.

'Then why *me*? If you're so convinced that I'm sexually active,' she spat, 'I should have thought it was the last thing you'd want to do!'

'But you've just finished assuring me that you're not,' he argued reasonably. 'We can always take precautions.'

'That is not the point!'

'No. The point is, we want each other. We're both free, both over the age of consent. Well over. Aren't we?'

'So?' she hedged.

'*Aren't* we?'

'Yes,' she admitted grudgingly.

He smiled, touched one long finger to her neck, making her shiver. 'Come on, admit it. You want me as much as I want you.'

'Yes. No. Oh, I don't know, do I? We have to *wait*!'

'All right,' he agreed.

'What?' Swinging round, she stared at him.

He gave a mocking smile. 'I agreed with you. Come on.'

Bewildered, shaken, she just stared at him. 'Come on where?'

'Out.'

'Out?'

'Mmm. I'll show you the countryside.' That mocking smile still playing about his mouth, he tugged her out and down to the courtyard.

Totally nonplussed, she climbed obediently into his Land Rover when he held the door open for her, settled herself in her seat, fixed the seat belt, and just stared blankly through the windscreen. 'You were aroused,' she accused him stupidly, and as though she found the whole thing totally incomprehensible.

'Still am,' he agreed cheerfully.

'Then how can you...?'

'Control.'

Control? Never mind her ribs, her heart, her lungs—even her *toes* ached! Didn't his?

He fired the engine, drove out of the courtyard, and up towards the tree line.

'Right. Geography lesson,' he began briskly as he drove. 'Dartmoor fills the belly of Devon, but on the northern edge, lying across the border with Somerset, is Exmoor. Lower, gentler than Dartmoor, it is underlain not by granite but by more conformist slates, grits and sandstones which outcrop only rarely. These rocks have weathered into softly swelling hills, their heathery summits seldom above fourteen hundred feet. Dunkery Beacon is the highest, overlooking the lush oasis of Porlock Vale and the wooded combes which cut deep into the uplands.'

'Will you stop talking like a guidebook?' she protested crossly. 'And you haven't got your seat belt on.'

'No,' he grinned. 'I hate the damned thing. As I was saying, Exmoor is positively *fractured*,' he continued, unperturbed, 'with prominent valleys detaching the Brendons and the Selworthy ridge above Minehead. To the north, the hills run straight into the sea, forming some of the most glorious cliff scenery in Britain. You can walk for miles along the sheep-grazed, hump-backed ridge that follows the coast—'

'I don't want to walk along sheep-grazed tracks! I *hate* sheep-grazed tracks!'

'Then where shall we go? Dunster? With its medieval village? Tarr steps—considered to be Britain's oldest and longest stone clapper bridge? Although, I have to confess that in the floods of fifty-three—or was it fifty-four? No matter—it was swept away, and we're not entirely sure it was put back in the proper order. However, it's been numbered now, so if it happens again—'

'Carrick!' she warned ominously.

'And Tarr, probably a corruption of the Celtic *tochar*, means causeway. Or we could go to Withypool, The Chains—now that *is* worth looking at. The loneliest stretch on Exmoor, a boggy plateau reaching to almost sixteen hundred feet...'

'Fascinating,' she said tartly.

'Pinkworthy Pond is in the middle.'

'How exciting.'

'And, on an August night in 1952, during one of the most violent rainstorms ever recorded in Britain, the water, unable to soak in, poured off the moor in angry, boiling torrents to form the catastrophic flood which descended on the fishing port of Lynmouth, mowing down everything in its path and sweeping cars and boats far out to sea. Want to go back and make love yet? I know it hasn't been a week, although it certainly *feels* like it.'

Staring at him, totally undermined by the quirky smile he was offering her, feeling her heart jump in her throat, Kenda quipped weakly, 'It feels like a month.'

Bringing the Land Rover to a gentle halt, he set the handbrake and turned to face her again. One arm along her seat-back, bringing his face much too close, he asked with a rueful smile, 'Was that a yes or a no?'

Feeling hot, uncomfortable, she gave a funny little sigh, pressed her hands together and closed her eyes, gave a little start when she felt his mouth touch her closed lids, a tongue trail damply across her lashes.

'Oh, God.'

'That's what I was thinking.'

'Oh, Carrick.' With a helpless little laugh, she opened her eyes, stared into his amused grey ones.

'I don't think I have *ever* wanted a woman as I want you,' he confessed softly. 'I couldn't forget you. And the dear Lord knows I tried.'

'And you hate yourself for it?'

'Not any more. I think, Kenda McKinley, that you are a fraud.'

'Fraud?'

'Mmm. Not *nearly* as tough as you pretend. And I do so *hate* cold showers.'

Still staring into his eyes, she swallowed drily, licked her lips—then hastily abandoned the exercise when she saw his eyes move to them, registered the slight flush of warmth along his cheekbones. 'It isn't going to go away, is it?' she asked huskily.

'No.' And his denial sounded almost like a groan.

'Let's go back,' she whispered—and the Land Rover was in gear and moving almost before she'd finished speaking.

They hadn't gone far, and it didn't take them long to return, and all her worried little talks to herself on that short journey—about promiscuity, shame—didn't do any good at all. She *wanted* him. She didn't think she had ever wanted anything more in her life. And if it was wrong, foolish, then it would have to stand as testimony to her desire, because she wanted him so badly that she felt ill.

He slammed the car to a halt, tugged her up the back stairs and into his quarters. Kicking the door shut behind him, he stared at her, began to laugh, hauled her forcefully into his arms.

'*Wretched* girl.'

'I've been called worse.'

'And with less provocation?' he asked gently.

'Mmm.' Curling her hands into his sweater, she gave a funny little smile. 'Would you believe I *never* behave like this?'

'If you'll believe that I don't.'

Yes, she definitely believed *that*, and as she stared at him, remembered the way he had kissed her in the corridor, remembered how it had made her feel—that little blink of surprise in her head, that churning in her stomach—she knew she could no more deny him than prevent night following day. Hands clenched compulsively in his sweater, heat curdling her insides, dismissing thoughts of wrongness, she touched her mouth to his—and the spark was ignited.

He wasn't gentle. Neither was she. He dragged her sweater over her head, tossed it aside, dragged off his own, and, his eyes never once leaving hers, he pulled her back against him, hissed as flesh met flesh. And if he'd wanted her as much as she'd wanted him, as his actions now proved, then how on earth had he managed to give a dissertation on the countryside without his voice even wobbling?

And then thoughts of countryside, and anything else, disintegrated as his mouth bent to ravage hers, his thumbs to probe the fullness of her breasts as he sought and found the centre fastening of her bra and released them. Withdrawing slightly, eyes holding hers, he removed the scrap of lace and tossed it to the floor.

'I feel—hot,' he said thickly as he cupped each full breast in his palms, held them against his naked chest. 'A veritable furnace.' And then he smiled— a quirky, crooked, so damnably attractive smile— and she was lost. 'Don't look so tragic,' he ordered softly as he moved his hands down over her ribcage. 'And I *hate* women in tight jeans,' he complained as he fought to undo the metal button.

'Do you?' she asked dazedly as she in turn began to explore the warmth of him, the heat, to revel in the feel of firm, silky flesh beneath her fingers, admire the contrast of pink nails against tanned skin, until she felt faint, and so very wanton. Leaning forward so that her nipples brushed him, she began to press kisses to his collar-bone, his throat, until he groaned, brought her to a halt.

'Martin might come in?' she breathed as she licked the perspiration that beaded his neck.

'He knows better,' he growled. Halting his attempts to divest her of her jeans, he slid one hand behind her neck, pulled her mouth towards his, and kissed her with a rough mastery that left her breathless. Before she could recover, he scooped her up in his arms as though she weighed no more than a child and carried her through into his bedroom.

Holding her easily, despite the tension that racked him, he stared down at her face, her tangled hair, and then at her full breasts. 'I want you,' he said softly. 'So very badly. I *hurt*, Kenda.' Carrying her across to the bed, he laid her gently on the quilt, stood at her feet, pulled off her shoes, and, his eyes holding hers, tugged off her jeans. He removed his own, came to kneel above her on the wide bed.

'You're so astonishingly beautiful,' he murmured. 'So gloriously—wild.' It didn't actually sound like a compliment.

'So I've been told.'

'You don't think so?'

'No.' Lethargic, almost a spectator at her own seduction, she lazily raised one hand and touched her fingers to his mouth. 'Make love to me.'

'No.'

'No?'

'No. I've waited this damn long, I want to savour it. And don't smile like that. Don't—please—smile like that.'

Her smile widened. 'I should feel nervous,' she murmured softly as she trailed her fingers from his mouth to his throat, his chest and down to his flat stomach. 'Ashamed. At least *reluctant*!'

'Do you?'

'No.' Her eyes on her fingers, she touched the waistband of his briefs, felt the little shiver he gave and smiled again. 'You're aroused.'

'*Still* aroused,' he corrected her. 'Must be some sort of record.'

She gave a faint smile, found that she was shaking. 'Did you really want to know me all those months ago?'

'Yes.'

'That's why you offered me the job?'

'Yes.'

Watching him watching her, she swallowed, managed thickly, 'I want to see all of you.'

'Oh, God.'

'I want—'

'Don't,' he pleaded as he smoothed the material of her panties until it was taut, the thin silk revealing all that he wanted revealed. His breathing wasn't very steady, and that flush along his cheekbones was more hectic, much more noticeable. She suspected her own looked much the same. Certainly she felt very hot, and became hotter, wriggled involuntarily as he touched her.

Breath jerking in her lungs, eyes closed, head thrown back, she gave in to the wave after wave of sensation that assaulted her, pleaded, 'Not yet, not yet.'

Moving swiftly, his breathing laboured, he removed her panties altogether, removed his own briefs, tossed them to the floor, and lay above her. Elbows keeping his weight from crushing her, his mouth flirted briefly with hers, devastated her with a kiss too brief, tantalised her with a promise of what would come, then moved to explore other areas of her delightful anatomy until both were shaking uncontrollably, both breathing with the same staccato rhythm.

Her hands moved from his back to his hips, his buttocks, tried to press him lower. He resisted, continued to sensitise breasts already unbearably sensitive.

'Carrick,' she pleaded. 'Please.'

'No,' he denied thickly.

'*Please.*'

And he moved upright, repositioned himself, stared into her eyes as she wrapped her legs around his waist.

'I don't think my heart will take much more.'

'Nor mine,' he agreed raggedly as he slowly thrust towards her, into her, closed his eyes in an ecstasy of relief that changed so quickly to driving need.

Matching him, sharing, giving, unaware that her nails were clenched in his back, that her teeth were mangling his lip, her muscles locked rigid, she gave him all that she had to give, as she had *never* given, because she had somehow known from that poignant moment at the crashed plane that he was the one who would be perfect for her—the one man she could love. It did not matter at the moment that he did not love her back; *she* thought she loved him. An absurdity, but one that felt so right.

Lost in his own pleasure, he nevertheless ensured her own. A considerate lover, an experienced lover—but she didn't want consideration, she wanted fulfilment.

The pillows slid from the bed unnoticed; the duvet tangled as they rolled, moved, gasped, gave all the cries that lovers give when perfection is sought—and finally found. They reached the peak together, shuddered, held, then slowly slumped, relaxed. Breathing ragged, her face buried in his neck, eyes closed, she held him for what seemed like an eternity, as he held her, his mouth gentle and sweet against her hair.

Aeons later, when heartbeats had returned to near normal, when breathing had slowed, he raised his head, smiled down at her. 'Wow?'

Her own smile soft, gentle, loving, she nodded. 'Wow.'

He dropped a kiss on her nose, rolled easily to his feet, padded into the bathroom and fetched her a towel. 'Bath?'

'Please.'

He smiled, crinkled his eyes at her. 'It's big enough for two.'

'Good,' she said softly. Staring at him, examining him, eyes darker, sleepier, her lungs feeling bruised, she added huskily, 'You have a beautiful body.'

'So, Miss McKinley, do you.'

Returning to the bathroom, she heard him turn on the taps, heard the splash and rush of water, and sighed. Prayed. *This* time, she promised herself, it would be all right. *This* time she wouldn't mess up.

'Kenda?'

'Coming.'

Padding into the steam-filled bathroom, she halted, stared at him as he lay almost submerged, arms along the sides, head thrown back, eyes closed, and she felt her heart lurch. She wanted him for ever, she thought with a little lick of fear. For keeps. She knew with the utmost certainty that out of all the men in the world this was the one for her. And he didn't know. Probably would never know.

He opened one eye and smiled. 'Come on in; the water's fine.'

Stepping in between his legs, pushing away the pain, pretending for the sake of sanity that it was a light-hearted affair, she gingerly sat, let out her breath as the heat reached her, and lay back against his chest. He reached for the soap, lazily began to lather her breasts, and she wriggled in pleasure, and in pain, her eyes, which he could not see, filled with longing.

'Nice?'

'Mmm.'

Moving her hair aside, he examined the small scar on her shoulder, touched it with one gentle finger. 'Healing nicely.'

'Yes. Don't stop.'

With a little chuckle, he continued his soaping. 'Better?'

'Mmm.' Closing her eyes, she gave in to bliss, deliberately shut out thoughts of tomorrow. Of all the tomorrows.

'Don't go to sleep,' he warned.

'No.' But it was tempting. His hands were sure, competent as he continued to massage tense muscles, and she felt herself relax, give in to exquisite pleasure.

Smoothing her hands along his hard thighs, his knees, because she, too, needed to touch, she wriggled more comfortably against him, and she wanted to talk, she found. Just to talk. Nothing

specific, nothing world-shattering. Just to talk,
ramble amiably through any subject—history, art,
politics. Tell him how she felt. Only she couldn't
do that, could she?

'Carrick?'

'Mmm?'

'Are *you* going to sleep?' she demanded, and,
forgetting where they were, heaved herself over so
that water splashed everywhere, and stared into his
face.

'Do you have to be so damned impulsive?' he
spluttered as he shook his head to clear the water
from his eyes.

'Yes.' And then she grinned, because he was
beautiful, special—and life had to be lived *now*,
not on some nebulous promise of tomorrow.

Moisture beaded his skin, as it did hers, not only
from her abrupt movement, but because the water
was too hot. His lashes lay spiky and damp on his
cheekbones, his hair curling slightly against his
forehead and ears—and his mouth was less than an
inch from hers.

'Open your eyes,' she ordered, and he gave a slow
smile, obeyed, moved his palms to her lower back,
exerted gentle pressure.

'Not *again*!' she exclaimed on a laugh.

'Why not?' he asked lazily as he moved her gently
against him. 'Kneel.'

'There isn't room,' she protested weakly as excitement began to race through her, as wave after
wave of sensation swamped her.

'Try.'

Bending her knees so that they were either side
of his hips, she levered her upper body away from

him, lowered herself gently onto him, gasped, took a snatched little breath.

'Look at me,' he ordered.

She stared into grey eyes—such serious grey eyes, dark and compelling—and felt that shiver of desire that took away every other thought as he picked up the soap again and slowly began to lather her. Her neck, shoulders, breasts, arms, stomach. And his eyes never once left hers.

As her muscles involuntarily expanded and contracted, as a spiral of desire grew, flooded her, she bit her lip, moved against him, gasped at feelings that were so good, so right, so amazingly—erotic. And still their eyes held. A small nerve was jumping in his jaw, tension momentarily cramped his fingers as they gripped her thighs, and then he shuddered, sighed, reached to draw her against him, hold her tight, his mouth against her neck.

'Compulsive,' he muttered thickly. 'So damnably compulsive.'

'Yes.' Slowly easing her legs free, she lay atop him, curled her toes with his, rested her cheek against his strong chest, listened to his heart. Her hair, which she had intended to keep dry, got soaked, and she eventually raised her head, dripped on him, smiled, because she couldn't help herself. She smiled the most delightful, happy smile of an urchin child. And he stared at her, slowly echoed it. The smile became a grin, a bubble of laughter, and she threw back her head and laughed as she hadn't laughed for a very, very long time.

Shipping water with every movement, she framed his face with wet palms and kissed him hard on the mouth.

'You look like a rat,' he observed softly.

'But a very *happy* rat!'

'Good,' he smiled.

'Are you a happy rat?'

'A satiated happy rat,' he agreed. 'And the water's getting cold. And I do so *hate* cold bath water.'

'How very unromantic of you to say so when I'm sharing it.'

'But I can be extraordinarily romantic with a towel,' he promised.

'An offer too good to refuse.'

'Then get up.'

'I don't think I can.'

Martin called, and she found that she could. Extraordinarily quickly.

Carrick laughed.

'Carrick!' Martin yelled again. He sounded cross.

Getting out too, wrapping a towel round his hips, Carrick padded out and she heard Martin exclaim, 'What on earth have you been doing in there? Holding boat races?'

'No,' Carrick drawled. 'Seducing Kenda.'

There was a pregnant silence, and Kenda bit her lip, tried to stifle her laughter.

'You wanted me?'

'Yes! Didn't you hear the door?'

'No, I was busy. Who is it?'

'Hebsby.'

'Oh, hell. Tell him I'll be two minutes.'

'Tell him you were unavoidably detained, shall I?' Martin derided sarcastically.

Carrick laughed, and she heard him in the bedroom, dragging open cupboards and drawers. He sounded—happy.

Peeking out of the bathroom, making sure that Martin had gone, she grinned, then walked into the bedroom, a towel wrapped around her like a sarong. He smiled at her. 'I have to go out. Be about an hour. Drainage ditch,' he muttered obscurely as he dragged on clean jeans. He snatched up a sweat-shirt, grabbed a pair of socks and fled.

Well, she thought, if he was going to inspect a drainage ditch, his jeans weren't going to stay clean for long. He should have worn an old pair. How very practical and wifely—and her mood changed again, became sombre, because she doubted she'd ever be one. At least, not Carrick's.

Perching on the edge of his bed—a bed that had once been made with military precision, and now looked like a battlefield—she sighed, and Martin walked in, stood surveying her from the doorway.

She looked up at him, gave a lame smile. 'We've left an awful mess in the bathroom.'

'I'll clean it up in a minute.'

'You will *not*!' she argued, scandalised. '*I* will!' Then she sighed again.

'Another mistake?' he asked gently.

She nodded. 'Probably, only I sort of couldn't help myself. I think we're having an affair.'

'Only think?' he teased.

'Mmm. And you can take that smirk off your face,' she ordered softly.

'But I'm pleased,' he protested.

'Are you?' she asked doubtfully, with a little plea in her eyes which she wasn't aware of. 'You don't mind?'

'Good God, no!'

'It won't last,' she said sadly. 'I mean, he doesn't love me or anything.'

'Doesn't he?' he asked gently.

'No.'

'But you think you love him?'

She shrugged, gave a funny little grimace. 'I don't know. It *feels* like it. Sounds daft, I know, but I think I fell in love with him the first time I saw him. *Can* people fall in love that fast?'

'You're asking the wrong person,' he chided her gently.

'Yes,' she agreed on another sigh. 'How long do his affairs usually la—? Sorry, don't answer that. I don't really want to know, and even if I did it isn't fair to ask you, is it?'

'No,' he agreed. Walking into the bathroom, he began putting it to rights, and despite her protestations she absently watched him, her thoughts still on Carrick.

'Are you moving back?' he asked as he threw the wet towels into the laundry basket and began to mop the floor.

'Back? Into the dressing room, do you mean?'

He gave a small smile. 'Into *his* room, I meant.'

'Oh—no—I don't know. It all happened rather suddenly. I mean, that might be *it*, mightn't it?' she asked rather morosely.

'I doubt it,' he said drily. 'And shouldn't you dry your hair?'

'Hmm? Oh, yes, I suppose so.' But she didn't move, just continued to sit there. 'Do you think I'm a fool?'

'No,' he denied. 'I think Carrick is a very lucky man.'

Her face brightening, she asked eagerly, 'Do you?'

'Yes. Now go and get dressed before you catch a chill.'

With a little nod, she got to her feet, and, on impulse, trod softly across to him and pressed a warm kiss to his cheek. 'Thank you.'

Surprisingly, he blushed. 'What for?' he asked gruffly.

'Being so nice.'

Turning away, she hastily picked up her belongings, went pink as she rescued her knickers from the floor by the door, stuffed them into her jeans and fled back along to her own room.

You're a very silly girl, Kenda, she told herself, but the happiness just wouldn't go away, and as she dressed, dried her hair, she seemed quite unable to wipe the silly smile off her face. Or the hope. And the sun was shining, she saw. Feeling restless, eager, impatient, knowing she'd be unable just to sit waiting quietly until he came back, she decided to go for a walk.

Hurrying down to the kitchen to tell Martin where she was going, she found Carrick seated at the long table. Halting, she stared, felt suddenly shy, gave a lame smile. 'No drainage ditch?'

'Been postponed. He has to see a feed merchant first. Come here.'

Going pink, she walked slowly across to him, allowed him to pull her to stand between his thighs. Eyes crinkled with amusement, a smile on his mouth, he teased, 'Feeling awkward?'

'A bit. Despite what you've heard, I'm not very experienced at this sort of thing.'

'Good. Want to go for a walk? I'll show you the
red deer, the wild ponies—'

'OK.'

Slapping her rump, he moved her aside and got
up. Taking two coats from the hook just inside the
outer door, he tossed her one, shrugged into his
own, trod into muddy wellington boots and caught
her hand in his. Smiling down at her, he pressed a
swift kiss on her mouth. 'You're a delightful lady.
Come on, let's see if I can't change your mind about
the countryside.'

Did men fall in love with delightful ladies? Would
this man?

Walking outside with him, shivering a little in
the chill wind, she stared up at the blue sky. There
wasn't a hint of a raincloud to be seen, and she
smiled. She was quite willing, at that moment, to
be persuaded.

They were halfway up the hill when the sound
of a helicopter halted them. Shading his eyes,
staring upwards, Carrick cursed, then began to
laugh. 'Come on, the countryside will have to wait
for another day. We have visitors—and if *that*
doesn't persuade you to like the countryside,
nothing will.'

'The arrival of a helicopter will persuade me?'
she asked in confusion.

'Mmm-hmm.'

'But who is it?' she demanded when he began
tugging her back down again.

'You'll see.'

They reached level ground just as the helicopter
landed; they waited until the blades stopped

spinning, then walked to meet the tall, fair-haired man as he emerged carrying a long parcel.

She stared, hung back, opened her mouth in shock, and exclaimed in disbelief, 'That's Oliver Darke!'

'Mmm. And *don't* ask for his autograph!' he warned teasingly as he went forward to greet him.

Barely listening, she continued to stare at the world-famous actor, watched him pick his way across a boggy patch of grass and shook her head in disbelief.

'I don't know what it is,' Oliver exclaimed as he shook his shoes free of mud, 'but water seems to feature very largely in my life of late!'

Carrick laughed, pulled Kenda forward and introduced them.

Shaking the proffered hand, she smiled. 'Hello.'

'Hello.' And his voice was . . . to die for. Low and rich and throaty and—oh, boy.

'I think I'm in love,' she exclaimed weakly.

'With Carrick?' Deliberately misunderstanding, he smiled the smile that women would leave their lovers for, then chuckled. 'He's a lucky man.' Returning his attention to his friend, he grinned. 'Can't stop; have to get back to Paris and Vladivostok. Just dropped in to return the sword.' Handing across the package, he thanked him.

'You're welcome. Give my love to Paris.'

'After mine?' He smiled. 'Certainly. I haven't seen her for two days. A lifetime!'

'Then certainly after yours,' Carrick smiled back. 'And I quite understand why you won't even stop long enough to slake your thirst. And take very good care in that contraption. We've already had one mishap this week.'

'So I see,' Oliver muttered as he turned to look at the wreckage of the downed plane. 'Fatal?'

'No, thank goodness.'

He nodded, smiled again. 'Nice to have met you, Kenda. See you on the twenty-first?' he asked Carrick. 'You *are* coming?'

Carrick nodded, slapped him on the shoulder, tugged Kenda back away from the rotors.

Within a few minutes he was airborne, and they remained watching until he was out of sight.

'Impressive friends you have.'

'*Nice* friends,' he corrected her.

'Yes, not a prima donna.'

'Oliver?' he laughed. 'Good heavens, no!'

'And does he usually just—drop in?' she asked lightly.

'Sometimes. Impressed?' he mocked.

'Very. How did you meet?'

'Oh, years ago on a film set. In fact, I owe a lot of my success to him. He kindly recommended me to others, and to pay him back—' he smiled '—I taught him how to handle a sword for a television docu-drama on the Peninsular War.'

'Well, you might have warned me who was about to descend. I behaved like a no-brain.'

'True,' he grinned.

'Rat. Are we still going for that walk?'

'Yes—no,' he said as he pointed to a distant figure trudging towards them. 'Hebsby and the drainage ditch await. Sorry.'

'No problem. I'll go on my own.'

'Then stick to the paths, don't go far—'

'And don't talk to strange men,' she completed for him. 'I know.'

'And don't accept sweeties.'

With an infectious little gurgle of laughter, she tucked her hand in his arm and accompanied him to meet Hebsby. 'Why did Oliver have to get back to Paris?' she asked curiously. 'Filming?'

'Film...? No,' he laughed. 'Paris is his wife.'

'Oh. And Vladivostok?'

'His son,' he said softly, and with rather an odd note in his voice.

Halting, she stared at him, searched his eyes when he turned curiously towards her. 'You sounded...'

'Jealous? I am. If you could see them together...' Shaking his head, he urged, 'Come on; Hebsby will be getting impatient.'

Jealous because he wanted a baby of his own? Wanted a relationship like Oliver had, and didn't expect to have it with her? 'The baby isn't *really* called Vladivostok is he?' she asked as she hurried to keep up with his long strides. 'I mean, I know actors can be odd, but no one could be *that* unkind.'

'No, Nathan. Vladivostok is a private joke between him and Paris.'

'Is she nice?' she asked, almost wistfully.

'Extraordinarily.'

'I'm glad.'

'Are you?' he queried with an odd smile.

'Yes. I like people to be happy.' Turning, she smiled at the patiently waiting Hebsby, and he blinked, went red, mumbled something in return.

Carrick laughed, handed her the sword. 'Another scalp? Take that inside and give it to Martin, would you? I'll be about an hour.'

Nodding, clutching the long parcel to her chest, she watched them walk away. To be spoken of as Oliver had spoken of his wife... To be loved that much... To have Carrick's baby... Shutting it off, shutting it away, she turned and walked into the castle.

Giving the parcel into Martin's care, she told him she was going for a walk. 'Carrick's gone off with Hebsby.'

'You haven't had any lunch,' Martin reproved her.

'I'll have a sandwich when I come back,' she promised.

'Well, don't go far, and stay on the paths.'

'And don't accept sweeties from strangers,' she grinned. 'I know, Carrick's already given me a lecture.'

'How was Oliver?' he asked drily, and she gave a delighted laugh.

'Amazing! And I behaved like a no-brain.'

'Mmm, he has that effect on women, I believe.'

'Wretch.'

'Is it Tuesday?' he called after her.

Halting, she looked back, a puzzled frown on her face. 'Tuesday?'

'Mmm. You're being delightful.'

'De...? Oh.' She smiled. 'Yes, today can be Tuesday,' she agreed softly. Even though it was Friday. Her smile warm, appealing, she walked back to him and gave him a hug. 'Carrick said I was to stay away from you. But I don't think I shall.' With a roguish smile, she waggled her fingers at him and walked out, still grinning.

Turning in the opposite direction from the one she'd come in on, the soft, rather wistful smile still on her mouth, her collar turned up around her neck to keep out the cold wind and hands pushed into her jacket pockets, she strolled up to the tree line, walked through the tall oaks. A stream was chuckling somewhere to her right; chattering birds were busy about their daily work.

I've just met Oliver Darke, she told herself and Martin thinks I'm delightful. Did Carrick? Indulging in foolish little daydreams where babies featured largely, she wandered on without really taking in what she was seeing. Not half an hour ago, she'd felt gloriously satiated, happy, loved. And now... Now, she felt—restless, unfulfilled. She knew he didn't love her, of course, but if there was never hope, if you didn't take risks life never moved on. She wasn't promiscuous, had never been so, despite her proclivity for leaping without looking, but sometimes opportunity had to be grasped firmly...

Stop trying to fool yourself, Kenda, she told herself. This is an interlude. But he might grow to love her, mightn't he? He felt *compulsive* about her. Might that not grow into love?

Barely aware of her surroundings as she continued to think about Carrick, the way he made her feel, act, absently skirting boggy ground, deep puddles, she lost all track of time. It wasn't until she reached an open stretch of moorland, saw how low the sun was, that she turned to go back—which was when she heard a thwack followed by a whimper.

A frown on her face, she turned full circle, searching for the sound, and saw a dog being beaten. Without thought, outrage governing her actions, she practically threw herself down the slope, leapt a fallen tree, and, looking more like a Fury than a mortal, launched herself at the man, wrenched the stick out of his hand and broke it in half.

'How *dare* you?' she snarled. 'Whatever he's done, whatever he is, he doesn't deserve that!'

Recovering from his surprise, and with a fury to match hers, he snapped, 'This is sheep country!'

'I don't care if it's zebra country! You don't beat a defenceless animal!'

'You do when it worries sheep!'

'What sheep?' she demanded with a comprehensive gesture to encompass the empty field. '*I* don't see any sheep! And is the dog wearing a label saying "I'm a sheep worrier"?' she derided. 'No, he is not! And even if you had *proof*,' she shouted, 'you don't need to beat him! Only restrain him!'

'He's not *mine*!' he denied, sounding scandalised.

'Then that's even worse!'

'What the hell is going on here?' Carrick demanded from behind them, and they both swung round—Kenda with relief, the man with indignation.

'Is she with you?' he demanded.

'Yes,' Carrick agreed tersely.

'Then get her out of here! And if you've got *any* feelings of responsibility towards the community, teach her the rules of the land. You're a *warden*!'

'I know what I am,' Carrick drawled insultingly.
'I don't need you to tell me, or to point out my
responsibilities. Kenda, go home.'

Incensed, having expected help, she exclaimed,
'He was *beating* him!' Bending, she scooped up the
shivering, cringing dog, held him close. 'And I'm
not *with* anybody,' she added crossly. 'You expected me to stand by and let him be beaten?'

'I don't expect anything,' Carrick argued frostily.

'He's a puppy!'

'A stray,' he said dismissively.

'What's that got to do with anything?'

'It's sheep country.'

'Don't keep saying that! And even if it is that
doesn't make it right.'

'I didn't say it did.' Turning back to the man, he
raised one eyebrow, awaited explanation.

The man went red, glared his defiance. 'And now
I suppose you're intending to prosecute *me*!'

'Yes. Cruelty to animals is a punishable offence.'

'And sheep-worrying isn't, I suppose.'

'Do you know it was this dog?' Carrick asked in
the same hateful voice that was enough to terrify
a saint.

He glared at Carrick, glared at Kenda, turned on
his heel and stalked off.

'Well,' Kenda exploded, 'if that's the way country
people behave—'

'It isn't,' he denied curtly. 'And I told you to go
home.'

'I'm not a child, Carrick. You don't have to *order*
me.'

Staring at her, he said slowly and distinctly, 'You
could have been badly injured, not to say killed,

launching yourself at him the way you did. If he'd turned that stick on you . . .'

'So you saw, did you?'

'Yes, and before you berate me for not having helped sooner—'

'You're not helping me now!' she interrupted.

'Apart from any damage Taylor might have caused, you had no knowledge of whether the dog was dangerous or not.'

'He's a *puppy*!'

'A young dog,' he argued, hatefully pedantic, 'with sharp teeth and claws.'

'He was *beating* him!'

'I know. I saw.'

'Don't you even *care*?'

He sighed. 'Yes, Kenda, I do.' Plucking the dog out of her arms, he strode off, and with a fulminating glance at his back she hurried to catch up with him.

In no mood to understand that his anger might stem from his fear for her safety, she demanded. 'And the puppy?'

'I'll take him to the animal shelter.'

'You can't!' she denied, scandalised. 'He might belong to someone!'

'He doesn't.'

'How do you know?'

'Because I do!' he gritted, forging ahead.

Her face set, she followed, clambering over gnarled tree roots, soaked to the knees by grass and low bushes as she hurried to keep up with Carrick's long strides, muttering darkly to herself about selfish, arrogant, autocratic bullies. They eventually reached the castle and she followed him inside to the kitchen, and Martin. The elderly man turned, stared, kept his face straight with a supreme effort of will, glanced at the dog still held against Carrick's chest, then looked at Kenda's mutinous face.

'You've brought me a dog?' he enquired politely.

'Don't,' Carrick warned. Depositing the animal in Martin's arms, he turned to Kenda. 'What were you doing up by Taylor's field?'

'Walking!' she snapped shortly. Turning her shoulder on him, she began to tug the puppy's ears gently.

'To see?'

Flicking him a haughty glance, she queried icily, 'What?'

'Who did you go to see?' he asked stonily.

'*See?* I didn't go to *see* anyone! Why should I? I don't *know* anyone down here!' Glancing at Martin for enlightenment, and receiving none, she took the still shivering puppy into her own arms, cuddled him to her face, gently soothed him. The silence lengthened. And *she* wasn't going to be the one to break it, she determined.

'What are we intending to do with him?' Martin enquired interestedly.

Kenda snorted. 'Carrick wants to take him to the animal shelter!'

'And you don't?'

'No. And you *need* a dog in a castle this size, especially when it's so isolated.'

'I had a dog,' Carrick replied dampeningly as he stared at the bedraggled puppy without enthusiasm. 'It died.'

'Then you need another one,' she said positively.
'I think he's a wolfhound.'

'I can see what he is.'

'Irish. We could call him Murphy,' she
persevered.

'Original.'

The puppy wriggled forward, licked Carrick's
face and gave him a hopeful look. 'He likes you.'

'Gratifying.'

'Carrick! He *beat* him!'

'He'd lost sheep.'

'If I had my way, he'd lose *teeth*!' she grated.
'And you *can't* take the puppy to the animal shelter!
At least, not until he's recovered from his ordeal.
He's frightened, cold—'

'Flea-ridden.'

'Then I'll bath him!'

'Not in my bathroom, you won't.'

'Then *where*?'

'Out in the yard.'

'Don't be absurd! It's freezing out there! What
on earth is the matter with you? Did you expect me
to *leave* him?'

'Yes.'

'Yes, you would, wouldn't you? I can't believe
you're being so bad-tempered about this!' Mouth
tight, face stormy, she turned to Martin for support.
'He's very hungry.'

Martin gave her a humorously droll look, fetched
a dish from the cupboard, poured some milk into
it and set it on the floor.

Smiling her thanks, ignoring Carrick, Kenda
knelt and set the puppy down before it, watching

as he lapped it up with shivering enthusiasm. 'Poor little thing. How can people be so wretched?'

'If that was a crack at me—easily. And I'd hardly call him little!' Carrick derided. 'He's set fair to match a pony!'

'Which means he'll make an excellent guard dog.'

'There's no such thing as *good* guard dogs. This is sheep country, Kenda.'

'We can train him. And if just one more person tells me—'

'*We?*' he interrupted silkily.

'*I* will, then.'

He stared at her for some moments in silence, then drawled, 'And how long will that take?'

With a little stab of fear, because his words had sounded so—portentous, she glanced up at him and demanded defiantly, 'How long have I got?'

CHAPTER SIX

CARRICK let out an explosive sigh, turned and walked towards the staircase. 'I'm going to get cleaned up.'

Sitting back on her heels, Kenda stared at Martin, a bleak little frown in her eyes. 'I couldn't have *left* him,' she pleaded.

'No,' he agreed.

'So why is Carrick being so—horrible?'

'He's had a rough afternoon. And it was a wolf-hound that savaged some of our sheep not so long ago.'

'Oh. I didn't know.' Staring down at the puppy, who had come to nestle his head into her lap and raise pitiful brown eyes to her own, she sighed. 'He looks so . . .'

'Pathetic?' Martin asked drily. 'Go on, go and make your peace with Carrick; I'll find him something to eat.'

'I don't know if I want to make my peace with him! He didn't have to speak to me as though I were—'

'Kenda,' Martin warned softly. 'Go.'

'I have to bath him.'

'*I'll* bath him!'

Scooping up the puppy, she put him in Martin's arms, gave him the sort of smile that generally caused much havoc in her life, and walked slowly after Carrick. And *this*, she told herself sternly, is what comes of having an affair with someone you don't know! She knew he didn't love her, knew he only wanted a brief liaison; she just hadn't thought it would be *this* brief. And it was only a *puppy*, for goodness' sake!

She could hear the shower running as she entered his apartments, and, her face still set into lines of mutiny, she walked into his bedroom and perched on the end of the bed to wait. Her jeans clung wetly to her legs, stiff and uncomfortable, and she debated for a moment whether to go and change before she confronted him. And then it was too late, because he was walking out of the bathroom, stark naked, rubbing at his wet hair with a towel—and her heart dipped, jumped.

Fighting to hold it steady, she examined him, tried to be dispassionate, and failed. He had beautiful legs—long, well-muscled—and a magnificent torso—marred only by a long, angry-looking scratch on his chest. There was a deep graze down one arm, and a red patch on one knee. His head emerged from the towel, and he stared at her, his face grave, serious.

'You really only went for a walk?' he asked quietly.

'Yes. I said so.'

'And you didn't meet anyone?'

'No! Look, what *is* this?'

He continued to stare at her, shook his head. 'Nothing.' And then he smiled, and whatever he had said or done was forgiven.

Her sigh long and deep, bewilderment and the remains of temper on her lovely face, she asked quietly, 'You do *know* how I feel, don't you?'

'Yes.'

With a hollow laugh, she murmured, 'That sounded very cautious.'

'I'm a cautious fellow.'

Yes. 'And I suppose I'm now supposed to apologise for saving the dog's life?'

'No,' he said quietly.

'I didn't think you'd mind!'

'Didn't think at all,' he argued lightly.

'No,' she agreed. 'And is that such a terrible thing? Not to think? Is that why you were so cross?'

'No. I'd spent over an hour up to my neck in muck, nearly broke my back heaving rubbish out of the ditch because I was too impatient to wait for the tractor, because I wanted to get back to you for tea and sympathy, and then you weren't here— weren't eagerly awaiting my return covered in perfume and very little else. Martin was worried; you'd had no lunch...'

'I walked further than I intended,' she said stiffly.

He gave a quirky smile. 'Is that an apology?'

'No,' she returned, and his smile widened.

'And so I came looking. Spent another hour doing so—an hour in which I imagined you lying at the bottom of a ravine with a broken neck, an hour in which my ardour turned to anger, worry, exasperation. You weren't in the woods—of which I checked every damned inch. And then I heard you shouting. Not injured, not distressed—'

'I was distressed.'

'Angry,' he corrected her, 'covered in mud, and rescuing a bedraggled puppy who was getting all the attention I wanted.'

'Sorry,' she apologised. 'But I couldn't have left him.'

'No.'

'No?' she exclaimed. *'You* would have done!'

His smile turned wry.

'You wouldn't?'

He shook his head.

'You'd have done what I did?'

He nodded.

Unsure, hopeful, she accused him, 'But you'd have taken him to the animal shelter, wouldn't you?'

His smile ever wryer, a flame of laughter in his eyes, he asked, 'Does our future relationship depend on my answer?'

'Yes. No. You were so *angry.'*

'I was worried. Like a mother finding a lost child. Smack first. Then a hug.'

'I didn't *get* a hug!'

He laughed, held his arms wide.

Not moving, she stared into grey eyes that slowly lost their amusement, and asked soberly. 'How long *have* I got?'

'Oh, Kenda.' Lowering his arms, he tossed the towel aside, flattened his hair into some sort of order and came to sit beside her on the bed. Taking her hand in his, he looked down at their tangled fingers, then up into her eyes. 'Our—union,' he began seriously, 'wasn't a declaration of love.'

'I know that.' And however hard that was, however much she might wish it otherwise, she did know that.

'So, to answer your question, I don't *know* how long we have. Until the enjoyment, the warmth—dissipates, I suppose. Are you regretting it?'

'No,' she denied quietly.

'Then can we take each day as it comes?'

She gave a faint smile, nodded. She, who very rarely looked to the future, now wanted to do so. Wanted assurance. And assurance was the one thing she wasn't going to get.

'I want to make love to you,' he said softly.

Startled, she stared into dark grey eyes, felt her heart begin to thump, felt as though a band was slowly squeezing her ribs. 'Again?' she croaked.

'Again,' he agreed. 'And you have far too many clothes on for my liking. And, seeing as your current aim is only to do things that I like, you will go and remove them. Won't you?'

'Will I?' she managed thickly.

'Yes.'

Feeling mesmerised, heart beating like a triphammer, excitement curling her insides, she stood and walked into the bathroom on legs that felt decidedly unsteady. She wasn't entirely sure she believed his explanation, but she wasn't going to query it because where there wasn't love it was sometimes impossible to ask. And she didn't, really, want to know how long they had. Greedy for any morsel he cared to drop, she thought despairingly. Pride should have dictated she refuse the crumbs, but she couldn't. It was that shaming, and that simple.

Stripping off, she washed off any mud that had been deposited upon her during her adventure, and returned to the bedroom—as naked as he.

He was lying in the centre of the wide bed, arms folded behind his head and, as she approached, extended one hand to her, tugged her down beside him when she clasped it.

'Hello,' he greeted her softly, with one of his quirky smiles.

'Hello.'

'I'm sorry I was foul.'

'You're forgiven.' And such was his effect on her that she would probably have forgiven him anything.

'Banish the frown,' he ordered gently, 'and kiss me.'

Obedient, pliant, she leaned over him, pressed her mouth softly to his as he gently enfolded her in his arms, and this time it was slow, languorous, wholly delightful—so long as she didn't think.

Excitement built gradually as they lazily explored each other, exchanged indolent kisses, trailed warm hands across each other's flesh, tasted, touched, until need edged into their slow lovemaking, until passion drove out inertia. And she wanted to tell him so badly how much she loved him as they finally came together. And she couldn't, because he didn't want her love. And because something had made him angry.

Raising himself, curling her warmly against his side, he smiled into her eyes. 'No rushing away this time.'

'No,' she agreed softly.

'No urgent tasks to be performed, no need to get dressed, no need to move.'

'No.'

'Bliss. No need to talk; we can doze if we want to, take unashamed delight in each other's nakedness, trail fingers in exciting places, be abominably lazy.'

'Yes.'

'Except,' he added with an infectious chuckle, 'that I particularly want to watch something on television.' Stretching out his arm, he picked up the channel hopper from the bedside table, pressed a button to activate the portable set fitted into the corner of his bookcase, stuffed a pillow behind his head, curled her more warmly against him and gave *some* of his attention to a documentary about army manoeuvres in Norway.

'My old regiment,' he explained lazily. 'You don't mind?'

She doubted whether it would have made any difference if she had; anyway, she was curious to see the sort of things he had probably got up to when he'd been a member of the serving forces.

'Do you miss it?' she asked curiously as she watched young soldiers dressed in white camouflage gear scramble up mountains, ski across inhospitable terrain and dig holes.

'Sometimes,' he answered absently.

'And did you do things like that?'

'Mmm.'

'Why did you leave?'

'Cut-backs,' he murmured laconically.

'And would you have stayed in otherwise?'

'Maybe; who knows?'

Knowing that there was nothing worse than someone chattering when you were trying to watch something, she lapsed into silence, watched his profile instead, admired his straight nose, his determined chin, felt that low spiral of pain, need, yearning as she began describing lazy circles on his chest, stomach, until he put down the remote control, clasped her hand and raised it to his mouth.

'Want to go out for dinner?'

'If you like.'

'I do; I want to show you off.'

'Then I'd best go and make myself worthy of being shown,' she quipped.

He smiled, returned his attention to the television.

And it was that easy, she thought with a sad smile, for him to believe it was what she wanted. *All* that she wanted. Gathering up her clothing, making sure that Martin was nowhere to be seen, she scuttled back to her room to shower and dress. She shoved his earlier behaviour out of her mind because she couldn't afford to think about it, didn't want puzzles or innuendo; it nevertheless continued to nag at her.

Two hours later, clad in a clinging dress of mulberry wool, with black high heels and bag, and pearl earrings, her face carefully made-up, she collected her wrap and walked back to Carrick's quarters. He was wearing well-cut grey trousers, a grey-flecked sports jacket and a dark grey shirt and tie.

Suddenly and for no very good reason feeling embarrassed, she smiled and quipped, 'You look very smart.'

'Thank you—and you look exquisite. Ready?'

Nodding, wondering at the very slight withdrawal she felt in him, she waited for him by the door, then accompanied him down to the kitchen to tell Martin they were off. Murphy uttered a little yelp when she walked in, began thumping his raggedy tail on the floor, and if Carrick hadn't prevented him would have rushed across and jumped up at her.

'Stay!' Carrick said sternly, and with drooping ears and tail the dog slunk back to the blanket Martin had given him to lie on.

Opening her mouth to tell him not to be so severe, Kenda encountered his grey eyes and closed it again.

'Very wise,' he said drily. 'We won't be late,' he told Martin.

'And I'm to stay in and babysit the dog, am I?'

'Unless you're willing to court Kenda's temper by disposing of him, yes,' Carrick agreed, with an unrepentant smile. Taking her arm, he escorted her out to his Land Rover and helped her inside.

'Where are we going?'

'Lynton. A very nice restaurant overlooking the Bristol Channel.'

'Which, of course, I won't be able to see in the dark.'

'I'll describe it to you.'

Watching him, admiring him, feeling hopelessly out of her depth, she asked quietly, 'Is something wrong?'

'Wrong? No, what should be wrong?'

'I don't know; you just seem—different. A bit withdrawn.'

He smiled, turned briefly towards her. 'Then I apologise. Something's on my mind, that's all. Nothing to worry you.'

And nothing to do with her. Mistresses didn't have the right to probe—a fact that didn't stop her asking something else, despite her instruction to herself not to. 'Why did you ask if I'd met anyone on my walk?'

'No reason.'

'Yes, there was,' she argued. 'You expected me to meet someone. Who? One of your neighbours?'

'Did you?'

'No.'

'Good.'

'*Was* that why?' she persisted. 'You thought I might have been leading the local young farmers' association astray?' she derided somewhat waspishly.

'Maybe.'

'Carrick!'

'Well,' he drawled, 'you're probably the most delightful vision of womanhood they've seen in these parts for many a long year, and I don't particularly want lovelorn swains littering my doorstep night and day, do I?'

Before she could formulate an answer, and because she clearly didn't believe his glib explanation, he added, 'My immediate neighbour has a son who is, shall we say, a dedicated womaniser...?'

'And you'd prefer me not to add fuel to an already growing fire?'

'Something like that.'

And men seemed to find her the stuff of which dreams were made, however misguided that might be. Except Carrick. Had there been just a tinge of jealousy in his tone? No, she decided sadly, just a desire not to have his peace disrupted. With a little nod, she said, 'I promise to avoid all males under the age of—fifty?'

'Seventy.'

With a little chuckle, she nodded again. 'Seventy it is.'

'Thank you. My mind is greatly relieved.'

Watching him, examining that proud profile, she teased curiously, 'Were you worried for him, or me?'

'Him.'

With a gurgle of laughter, she turned once more to the front as the Land Rover climbed a steeply winding hill.

'The Victorians called this area Little Switzerland,' he explained as he reached the small town that was perched high on the clifftops.

'I can really see why.'

He smiled. 'Come in the daytime; you'll like it.'

'Will I?' she laughed. 'Sure about that, are you?'

'Positive.' Parking the car, he helped her out, settled her wrap warmly around her, hugged her to his side and hurried her along to the restaurant and out of the blustery wind.

'The decor matches my dress,' she giggled as he held a long velvet curtain aside for her to pass through.

'So it does.' He smiled at the head waiter as he hurried flatteringly over to them and, much to her surprise, introduced her.

'Carl, meet Kenda.'

'Delighted,' he beamed. 'Will you follow me?' Leading them to a small table tucked into the corner in front of a large, ornate mirror, he courteously seated Kenda, smiled once more at Carrick, and departed to collect the menus and wine list.

'You obviously come here quite often.'

'Now and again,' he agreed as he took a menu from Carl. Instead of opening it, he murmured, 'I expect you're hungry. You didn't have any lunch. Do you like seafood?'

'Yes.'

'Then will you allow me to choose?'

She smiled her acceptance, watched as he consulted with Carl and chose the wine. The restaurant was surprisingly busy.

'We get tourists all the year round,' explained Carrick, then gave a quirky grin. 'The current influx is because of the Beast.'

'Beast?' she exclaimed.

'Mmm. The Beast of Exmoor.'

Eyes wide, assuming a joke, she stared at him, and then a little memory filtered through. 'Cat,' she said. 'I remember reading about that. A puma, isn't it?'

'Possibly. That group at the far end,' he murmured, with a little movement of his head towards the far corner, 'are a film crew. They've been camping out on the moor for weeks!'

'Why are you laughing?'

'Because I don't believe it exists.'

'You've never seen it?'

'No, nor anyone else of my immediate acquaintance, although sheep *have* been savaged,' he admitted.

'Hence the ill-treatment of the puppy.'

'Mmm.'

Glancing towards the film crew, her attention was distracted by the billowing curtain at the entrance as someone entered, and idle curiosity turned acute as she recognised the blonde woman who came in.

'Lydia,' she murmured. She hadn't meant to say it aloud.

'Pardon?'

Snapping her eyes back to Carrick, she shook her head.

'You said "Lydia".'

'Yes,' she admitted. 'She just came in.'

He didn't turn, as most people would have done, didn't say anything else at all, merely gave her a long look.

'Martin told me her name when she came the other day,' she confessed.

'And what else did Martin tell you?'

'Nothing.'

He grunted. 'Martin seems to be getting very loquacious in his old age.'

'I asked,' she said defensively. 'It's natural to be curious, isn't it?'

A little gleam of humour sparked in his eyes. 'Entirely.'

'Stop being poky. She's coming over.'

'Then be polite.'

'I'm always polite. Until provoked,' she tacked on as she moved her eyes to the other woman. Slim and elegant, she made her way between the tables, her escort treading grumpily in her wake. 'She's with a man with red hair.'

'I'm interested?' Carrick drawled, and Kenda giggled, then turned it into a smile of welcome as Lydia reached them.

She gave Kenda a somewhat dismissive glance, and smiled at Carrick.

'Carrick! Just the person I need to see! A little sketch came in that I think might amuse you. Quite expensive, but—'

'Who by?'

'Joel Gilman.'

He pursed his lips, nodded. 'I'll call in later in the week.' Turning his head, he looked at her companion. 'Luke,' he greeted him, that little flicker of amusement back in his eyes.

'Carrick,' the man greeted him sourly, then turned and gave a deliberately provocative smile at Kenda. 'Who's the lovely lady?'

'My historian. Don't let us keep you.'

'No,' he agreed. Grasping Lydia's arm, he tried to force her away.

'I haven't finished speaking to Carrick!'

'Well, he's finished speaking to you! Move; you're blocking the aisle.'

With a cross 'tut', she moved on towards her own table, where a waiter was patiently waiting, chair held out in readiness.

Kenda gave a little smile.

'Don't,' Carrick warned.

'Don't what?' she asked innocently.

'*Anything.*'

'She likes you.'

'So does Martin,' he replied squashingly, 'but it doesn't mean I want him leaning over my shoulder when I'm eating. Tell me about the Roman legions.'

Her smile wry, she did so, and from there they argued amiably about other periods in history, art, plays, books they'd read and enjoyed, and all the while she was conscious of Lydia watching him, hating her because she was his current companion.

Kenda understood very well how she must feel. She knew she would have felt the same. And when it ended, as one day it must, would she be a brave soldier and walk away?

'What's wrong?' he asked quietly as coffee and mints were brought to the table.

'Nothing,' she denied, forced herself to smile, because how could she say that she was wondering what words he would choose to end the liaison? Or would she know without being told? Probably. But not just yet, please God. Not just yet, not just as she was beginning to know him better, to understand what made him tick.

They didn't hurry but lingered over their coffee, and although Carrick had only had one glass of wine because he was driving he didn't stint her consumption.

'Trying to get me drunk?' she teased.

He shook his head, smiled that quirky smile that always undermined her defences. 'I like my women—aware. You're blushing,' he laughed softly and in some surprise. 'How very delightful.'

'Especially for a woman so sexually active, do you mean?'

'No,' he said, his smile dying. 'For a woman I like very much. Ready?'

Nodding, wishing she could manage to keep her mouth *shut*, she thanked Carl for his excellent care of them, then, unable to resist one last look at Lydia and her companion, she accompanied Carrick back to the Land Rover and they drove home.

Her hand in his, she walked with him up to his quarters.

'Are you intending to commute?' he asked humorously as they halted outside his door.

'I don't know. Am I?'

'Whichever you prefer.'

She would prefer to be in his room, but if he didn't care one way or the other, she thought a trifle mutinously, then she would commute.

As though he knew very well what she was thinking, his smile widened. 'I'll go and warm the bed up.'

'I have to check on Murphy.'

'Murphy will be fine. Martin will take care of him.'

'Then I'll go and get undressed.' Marching along to her own room, and thinking that for two pins she'd stay there, she dragged off her clothes, threw them on the chair—picked her dress up and hung it on a hanger. It had been expensive!

And she couldn't for the life of her understand why women liked having affairs. There were so many complications! And surely it would be more gentlemanly to come to *her* room? She was beginning to feel like a cyprian! A kept woman of ill repute!

Disgruntled, and feeling somehow—cheap, she shrugged into her towelling robe, took off her make-up, and walked back to his quarters. If she hadn't wanted him so much, if her body hadn't been anticipating his lovemaking all evening . . .

'Move your things back here,' he said softly when she walked into the bedroom to find him already in bed.

'No.'

'Then stop sulking.' Holding back the covers for her, he waited, a mocking smile on his face.

'It's all right for you,' she grumbled. 'You're probably used to all this!'

'And you're not?' he asked gently.

'No.'

'How many lovers have you had?'

'One,' she stated defiantly.

'And how many near misses?'

'Two. How many have you had?'

'Mind your own business,' he ordered provokingly. 'I don't kiss and tell. Come to bed.'

'And do I return to my own when we've made love?'

He leaned forward, grabbed her hand, dragged her into the bed and covered her up. Leaning over her, staring down into her cross face, he grinned. 'Who said anything about making love?' Before she could answer, think of a stinging retort, he kissed her. 'Although now that you mention it...'

'I don't find this easy, Carrick!'

'I know. And you talk too much, think too much—wear too much.' His hands swift and sure, he untied her robe, parted it, ran his hands down her warm flesh until it came up in goosepimples.

And despite her irritation with him it was as good as ever, as beautiful and satisfying as ever.

Curled warmly in his arms, still with that little worry in her mind that she shouldn't be doing this, she drifted into sleep, only to wake less than an hour later when the door was flung open and bright light flooded the room.

'What the devil...?' Carrick began angrily, and then just stared in sleepy exasperation as Martin

marched into the room carrying the puppy still
tangled up in its blanket.

'*You* try sleeping with the racket he's making!'
Dumping Murphy on the bed, dressing gown
flapping, Martin stalked out and slammed the door
behind him.

Cursing, Carrick grabbed the puppy by the scruff
of the neck and deposited him on the floor. 'Stay!'
he ordered.

Murphy let out a howl of anguish, scampered
round to Kenda's side and scrambled up. He was
shivering violently.

'He is not sharing the bed!'

'He's frightened.'

'I don't care if he's dying! He is not sharing the
bed. Apart from the fact that he's probably full of
fleas—'

'Martin *bathed* him!

'—he's not house-trained,' he continued harshly.
'And if you're prepared to put up with a wet bed
I'm not. Take him down to the hall.'

'You can't banish him to the hall! It's freezing
down there!'

'Then give him a cushion to cuddle.'

'Don't be so heartless!'

'Then you go and cuddle him! I mean it, Kenda;
I am not having that flea-bitten shagbag sharing
my quarters. You should have taken him to the
animal shelter.'

Face grim, putting Murphy on the floor, where
he immediately began to howl, she dragged her robe
out of the bed, shrugged into it, tied the belt with
a yank that nearly split the material, scooped up

Murphy, snatched his blanket off the bed and stalked out.

'And don't sleep in the lounge with him,' he called after her. 'The rugs are Persian!'

'I don't care if they're Russian!' she yelled back.

Stalking through the lounge, slamming the outer door, she marched along to her room, collected the duvet off the bed and stormed down to the hall. Arranging the blanket on the hearth, she gently deposited the dog on it, then bent to make up the fire. Dragging a log from the pile, she shoved it on, poked it angrily, then dragged one of the chairs as near as she could get, arranged her duvet on it and plonked herself down.

If she'd known he wasn't an *animal* lover... You always assumed people who lived in the country *liked* animals! 'Shut up,' she told Murphy as he continued to howl. 'I'm not in the least impressed. Settle down and go to sleep.' He cocked his head, stared at her with an expression of hurt entreaty, and put his nose on his paws.

With a crotchety sigh, she pulled the duvet more warmly round her, tucked her neck into the folds as a stray draught found exposed skin, and, scowling at the fire, continued to catalogue all Carrick's faults.

Despite the discomfort, the fact that one side of her was roasting, the other frozen, she drifted into sleep—and woke to find her feet resting comfortably on a footstool, a thick rug enfolding her from neck to toe. A guard had been safely placed round the fire, and a lacquered screen set to shield her from the draughts.

Murphy was curled in his blanket, tail over his nose. In no way mollified by these comforts, she scowled at a pair of crossed swords that decorated the far wall. It was light, but she had no idea what the time was because there was no clock in the hall. Not that it mattered, she supposed.

Hearing movement, she turned her head and watched an abnormally straight-faced Martin as he walked in carrying a tray holding coffee-pot, cup, sugar bowl and cream. He placed it almost reverentially on the end of the long table.

'Don't ask me if I slept well,' she warned.

His lips twitched.

Hearing the sound of her voice, Murphy woke, stretched, wagged his tail and walked over to the outer door.

'Well!' she exclaimed. 'Not house-trained, is he?'

'But probably not sheep-trained,' Martin said softly as he walked across to let the dog out into the enclosed courtyard. 'If you take him out, make sure he's on a lead.'

'I don't have a lead! And anyway, Carrick will probably make me take him to the animal hospital.'

'*Make* you?' Carrick asked quietly from somewhere behind her.

Craning her neck round, she scowled. 'You made me come down *here*,' she stated grumpily. Disentangling herself from her covers, she sat up to pour herself some coffee, then held the cup in her palms to warm them.

The dog scratched to come in, and after Martin had opened the door, walked straight over to Carrick and stood before him wagging his tail.

'Knows which side his bread's buttered, doesn't he?' Martin observed blandly as he walked back towards the kitchen.

'Sit!' Carrick ordered, and, not at all to Kenda's surprise, Murphy did. 'And I utterly refuse to call him Murphy!'

'Dublin, then,' she said, softly conciliatory.

He grunted. 'I'm sure the residents of Dublin would be delighted to know that a mangy piece of fur had been named after their fair city.'

'He isn't a mangy piece of fur. When he's been brushed, fattened up a bit...' Peeping at Carrick sideways, she murmured softly, 'We'll keep him, then, shall we?'

Without answering directly, he said, 'You'll need a lead, collar, basket, brush... And he'll need to be trained.'

'We also need to find out who dumped him.'

'Already done,' he said dismissively.

'So you *did* care! I hope they prosecute him!'

'He'll be fined.'

'Who was it?'

'Never you mind; I don't want you adding your twopenny-worth and causing yet more trouble.' With a faint smile, he asked, 'Sleep well?'

'Yes,' she agreed airily.

'Liar,' he reproved her softly. 'Go and get the dog's things this morning whilst I'm out. I should be back by eleven; I'll take you sightseeing.'

'What an inducement.

'*I* thought so.'

After a brief internal struggle, she relented, grinned. 'Well, I hope we get further than we did last time.'

An amused light in his eyes, he asked softly, 'Do you?' Walking after Martin, he halted, stared at the dog who was following him. 'Stay,' he said sternly. And, leaving Murphy in a dejected heap on the floor, he walked off.

'Traitor,' she scolded the animal. '*I* was the one who sat up with you all night.'

Finishing her coffee, she collected up her duvet and the cover that Carrick had presumably put over her, told the dog to stay without any confidence that he would obey her and started up to her room—only to halt halfway. With a soft curse, dumping the bedclothes where she stood, she hurried back down, nearly fell over Murphy, righted herself, and hurried into the kitchen.

'Carrick,' she began urgently, and he turned from the stove where he was frying bacon. 'Can you—um—let me have an advance on my salary? I'm nearly out of petrol.'

'How low are you?'

'Very low.'

'OK, I'll leave a can by your car. The nearest garage is at Barbrook; you can fill up there. They take credit cards.'

'I haven't got one,' she said bluntly, and with a rather defiant glitter in her eyes.

'Haven't got one?'

'No.' Embarrassed, she refused to explain that she'd cut hers up when she'd lost her job. Afraid of getting into debt, she'd taken the only sure way out—disposed of it. 'And I need some other things as well. I mean, apart from what I have to get for the dog.'

'We do have banks in Devon.' He smiled.

'I dare say you do!' she stated crossly. 'So can I borrow some or not?'

Giving her a surprised glance, he narrowed his eyes and frowned. 'Nothing in the bank?'

'No.'

Searching her face, he asked gently, 'How much do you need?'

'Twenty will do,' she mumbled awkwardly.

Putting down the spatula, he reached into his back pocket for his wallet, handed it to her. 'Take fifty; better to have too much than too little.'

'Thank you.' Avoiding his eyes, she added, 'If you could take it out of my salary, I'd be grateful.'

Replacing his wallet in his pocket, he turned back to his bacon. 'How have you been managing without money?' he asked quietly.

'With a great deal of difficulty,' she retorted flippantly, to cover her embarrassment. 'I'd better go and get dressed.'

'And stop that hound from howling.'

Nodding, she hurried away, admonished Murphy to behave himself, and went up to get showered and dressed. She didn't think she had ever felt so mortified in her entire life. And if it hadn't been for Richard... Clamping her mouth tight, she returned to the kitchen to get herself some breakfast. Carrick had gone, and Martin had taken over stove duties.

When she returned to the castle, it was to find Carrick's Land Rover already in the courtyard, and after parking beside it, she carried her purchases inside. He was in the kitchen, staring somewhat pensively from the window, a cup of coffee clasped in his hands.

He turned, smiled. 'Coffee?'

'Please.'

'Get everything you needed?' he asked as he went to pour her one.

'I think so.' Setting her purchases on the floor, ruffling Murphy's ears when he came to investigate, she removed the brush, knelt and began to groom him. Carrick watched her ministrations, a rather sardonic smile on his mouth.

When she was finished, she fitted his collar, drank her coffee and declared herself ready for any adventure.

'Where are we going?'

'Clovelly.'

'Which is?'

'A fishing village.'

'Wow.'

He shook his head at her, rinsed out the cups, clipped Murphy's lead to his collar and handed it to her with instructions not, on any account, to let go of it. Then he shrugged into his wax jacket and led the way out.

Encouraging Murphy to jump into the back of the car, Kenda took her place beside Carrick and, with a faint smile on her face, prepared to be excited.

He gave her a brief potted history of the places they passed through, his voice laconic, amused.

'Westward Ho!' she exclaimed in delight as she read a signpost. 'Is that where we're going?'

'No, but the rector of Clovelly was the father of Charles Kingsley, who wrote the book and thereby helped to make the village famous.'

'I didn't know that!'

'You learn something every day,' he murmured in amusement. Pulling off the road and into a car park, he parked in front of a low building proclaiming itself to be the visitors' centre and with Kenda firmly clasping Murphy's lead went inside, where he paid.

'You have to *pay* to visit the village?'

'Mmm, helps towards its upkeep.' Catching her free hand in his, he led her through the centre and out to a steep lane. Donkeys stood in a field to their left and she halted to admire them.

'Where's the village?' she asked curiously.

'Thataway,' he explained, pointing ahead.

All she could see *thataway* were trees, shrubs and, in the distance, the sea.

'If you don't fancy the walk, either up or down, there's a Land Rover service.'

Not understanding, she shook her head. 'I'm quite happy to walk.'

He gave another smile that she didn't understand, led her through a small gate, along a path— and there, spread out below her, was the village. It cascaded down the cliff like a waterfall.

'Good heavens,' she exclaimed weakly.

'Quite. Still want to walk?'

'Yes, of course. Do people still *live* here?'

'Mmm.'

'Then I pity the poor postman!'

'Everything is delivered by sled,' he explained in amusement as he led her downwards. 'Watch your feet, the cobbles are slippery.'

Grasping his hand more firmly, wishing he'd had the forethought to warn her to wear rubber-soled shoes, she slowly descended the winding cobbled steps with him. There were whitewashed cottages covered in ivy, window-boxes which, in summer, would no doubt be full of flowers; she stared about her in delight.

After one or two side-trips to see St Peter's Chapel and peek into the craft shop, and with Murphy investigating interesting scents every five minutes, they finally reached the bottom.

'Fourteenth-century quay,' Carrick pointed out.

'Can we walk along it?'

'Of course. Give me the lead; you might need both hands.'

Obeying, she walked with him along the ancient stones and, with his help, climbed down into the lee of the wall, where they sat for a while out of the wind, in sunshine that felt quite warm, and stared at the lifeboat station, the tiny harbour.

'It was the sea and its once-flourishing fishing industry which gave the village its birth. First settled in the Iron Age, it's mentioned in the Domesday Book.'

'It doesn't look real, does it? Like something from a film set.'

'Mmm. Lunch?'

Smiling her agreement, she followed him back to the shore, carefully negotiated the uneven cobbles, smiled at two lifeboatmen who were standing by a collection box, popped in two pound coins, earned

their admiration and their thanks and, knowing
they were watching her, followed Carrick into the
Red Lion.

'I thought you didn't have any money,' he queried
with a smile.

'I don't. It was yours.'

He laughed, shook his head.

'I always give to the lifeboats. And Poppy Day.'

'And it's always better to give someone else's
money away,' he teased, and was surprised when
she looked mortified. 'Hey, it was a joke.'

'Yes, I know, but I... Well, I don't like
borrowing!'

'No,' he agreed. 'I doubt anyone does. Come on.'

When they'd eaten, and with the sky beginning
to cloud over, he asked, 'Want to walk back or get
the Land Rover?'

'Walk.'

'Sure?'

'Yes. You do have a poor opinion of us town-
dwellers, don't you?'

He smiled, refused to answer, and, when they
were ready, walked slowly—very slowly—back up
the steep cobbled street. Carrick wasn't even the
slightest little bit out of breath, and she got the
feeling that he could have *run* up them if he'd
wanted to, if he hadn't had to wait for her.

They drove home by a different route, and she
knew he watched her, waited for her reaction to the
scenery, the isolation of some of the villages.
Refusing to be drawn, content in his company, with
Murphy sitting in the back, his head on her
shoulder, she remained silent.

It was dark when they arrived home, and just beginning to spit with rain, the earlier sunshine only a memory.

They ate in the kitchen, after which Carrick excused himself.

'I have some things to sort out in the armoury. I'll see you later.'

Leaving Murphy in the kitchen with Martin, she settled herself in the lounge with her notes on Roman legions.

Warm, sleepy, her mind miles away, she was startled when Martin thrust open the door and announced portentously, 'RCM is here!'

'RCM?' she queried in confusion.

'Yes. Richard... "Cheating"... Marsh!'

CHAPTER SEVEN

'No!' KENDA exclaimed. Tossing down her book, she repeated flatly, 'No.'

'Too late,' Richard said tightly from behind the older man. 'I want to talk to you!'

'Well, I don't want to talk to you!'

'Tough!'

'You *cheated* me!' she yelled furiously as she scrambled to her feet. 'You stole my manuscript and were having it published under your own name! And don't pretend you weren't! I read the letter! And if you don't want another example of what I do to cheats I suggest you leave now! Martin, show him out!'

'Martin isn't showing anyone out until I've talked to you!' Brushing one hand through his thinning fair hair, his blue eyes unaccustomedly bright with temper, he exclaimed, 'You *ruined* my clothes! Gave the hotel staff untold amusement! Caused me a great deal of grief and expense—'

'So see my lawyer! And it took you long enough to come and complain about it!'

'I don't want to see your lawyer! Even if you had one, which you don't—'

'Get to the point!'

'The *point* Kenda,' he enunciated furiously, 'is that, as usual, you went off half-cocked! If you had waited for an explanation—'

'Hah! There *is* no explanation! And it took you long enough to come and proffer one!' Unaware that Martin had left them, unaware of anything except her anger at Richard's presumption in coming here, she spat, 'I *trusted* you!'

'With very good reason!' he spat back. 'Because I am *trustworthy*!' Removing an envelope from his pocket, he practically threw it at her. 'Open it!'

'No! You think I might actually want to *congratulate* you?'

'Open it!' he snarled.

When she refused, when she only continued to glare at him, her colour heightened, her eyes narrowed in fury, he snatched it back, tore it open and unfolded the letter it contained. 'Read it! Read it, Kenda,' he ordered more quietly.

Snatching it from him, she stared at it, barely took in what it said, frowned, and read it again. 'It has my name on it!' she accused him.

'I *know* it has your name on it!'

'Not your name. Mine.'

'Yes.'

Lifting her eyes to his, she sneered, 'You had it changed because you were afraid I might sue you? Afraid it might come out in court that you stole my manuscript?'

'No.'

'Then why? In the hotel, the letter, *this* letter, or one very like it, had *your* name on it.'

'Yes. A mistake. As you would have found out if you'd bothered to ask me instead of mutilating my wardrobe.'

'Publishers don't make mistakes,' she contradicted him flatly.

'Don't they?'

'No.' But uncertainty was creeping in, a feeling of shame and horror. 'Did they?' she asked quietly.

'Yes. I gave them your manuscript to read; they didn't bother with or didn't take in the title page and assumed it was mine. They liked it, wanted it, and so I had the acceptance letter sent to the hotel as a surprise for you. Some surprise,' he added scathingly. 'You now owe me the better part of five hundred pounds—the amount it cost to replace my wardrobe.'

Staring at him, she opened her mouth, closed it again. 'That's why we went to the hotel for the weekend and didn't come straight here?' she asked slowly.

'Yes,' he agreed tersely. 'I thought, in my stupidity, that we could have a nice, private little celebration. I'd arranged a special dinner. *Candlelit*,' he spat in self-disgust.

'Oh, Richard!' she exclaimed helplessly. Remembering what she had done, the damage she had caused, she bit her lip. 'I didn't damage your golf clubs,' she said placatingly.

'No, only emptied them out of the window. Thank you *so* much!'

'They really liked it?' she asked hesitantly.

'Yes,' he agreed shortly.

'Want to publish it?'

'Yes.'

'I thought—'

'I know what you thought, and don't *ever* ask me to do anything for you again!' Turning on his heel, he walked out.

'Wait!' she yelled urgently. Tossing down the letter, she hurried after him, grabbed his arm, made him stop. Tugging him round to face her, she stared into his set face.

'I thought... Truly a mistake?'

'Yes.'

'Oh, Richard. Oh, Richard, I'm so sorry. When the courier brought it, when I saw the publisher's name on the envelope, when I opened it, saw your name—'

'You shouldn't have opened it at all! It was addressed to me!'

'I know, but... It wasn't sealed,' she excused herself weakly, 'and I was so eager to know! You were always so evasive whenever I asked you about it. Every time I mentioned it, asked if you'd given it to a publisher, you kept fobbing me off. I thought you didn't like it, thought it not worth publishing, or that the publishers had been scathing, and then, when I saw the envelope, read the letter, saw you named as the author...'

'I "fobbed" you off, as you put it,' he said distastefully, 'because I wanted it to be a surprise, wanted to wait until the deal was finalised. They want you to ring them, and arrange a meeting, discuss the contract. Naturally *I* couldn't do so!' Removing her hands from his sleeves, he turned and would have walked off if she hadn't grabbed the back of his jacket. Scurrying round to stand in front of him, she stared into his averted face.

'I'm sorry,' she said pleadingly. 'Oh, Richard, don't be angry; I didn't know. How could I have known?'

'You could have asked!'

'I don't ask! You know I don't! You *know* what my temper is like!'

'And that *excuses* it?'

'No, but I—'

'You cut up my *clothes*!'

'I know,' she said softly, winningly, and gave him a tentative smile. 'I was cross.'

'You were demented! You left the scissors in my *shoes*!' he exclaimed, as though he'd never heard of such a thing. 'And if that wasn't bad enough, before I had a chance to clear up, the manager came to call! Came to ask if everything was all right, because Miss *McKinley*,' he emphasised, 'had just walked out and seemed upset! *Upset?*' he demanded of himself. 'Miss McKinley doesn't get *upset*! Oh, no, Miss McKinley gets completely and utterly out of control!'

Her lips twitched, and, trying for peace, forgiveness, she slid her hands up his chest, rested them against the lapels of his jacket, gave him a rueful, wheedling smile.

'The manager thought we were *lovers*!' he exploded in remembered embarrassment.

So had Carrick, but she didn't think it wise to tell him that. 'Sorry,' she murmured.

'*Lover?* I wouldn't have you as a lover if you were... Even if I didn't love my wife! And it doesn't surprise me in the *least*,' he continued, goaded, 'that you don't have any friends—'

'I do have friends,' she argued half-heartedly.

'No, you don't! You have people too terrified to cross you! I took you into my house!'

'I know.'

'Supported you, encouraged you...'

'I know.'

'And what thanks do I get? Abused, humiliated—'

'I'm sorry.'

'I won't *ever* help you again, Kenda! Not *ever*!'

'I'll share my royalties with you,' she promised.

'I don't want to share your royalties. And the royalties will probably be negligible.'

'Then I'll dedicate the title page to you.'

'I don't want it dedicated to me.'

Sliding her arms round his neck, she pressed a soft kiss to his chin. 'You like me really.'

'I do *not* like you! You're a wretched, terrible person!'

'I know.'

'I was so *angry*, Kenda! I nearly didn't come at all! I went back to London, furious and disgusted, and for two pins I *would* have had the manuscript published under my name, just to *show* you! But *I'm* not unprincipled!'

'I know; you're a very nice person, the very best friend anyone could have.'

'Not any more,' he denied, but the stiffness had gone out of him, and the rigidity in his muscles. With something that nearly approached a smile he put his arms around her, held her loosely. 'Being a friend to you is *dangerous*!'

'Exciting.'

'*Dangerous!*' he insisted.

Smiling at him, pressing another kiss to the corner of his mouth, she said softly, 'Carrick said I should carry a government health warning.'

'Carrick is right! In fact, you should be locked up! And if someone sees you kissing me I'll probably end up in the divorce courts, which would *really* make my life complete!'

'I won't tell a soul,' Carrick drawled from behind them.

They broke apart, more in surprise than out of any feelings of guilt. Richard blushed; Kenda gave him a smile.

It wasn't returned.

'Differences sorted?' he enquired smoothly.

'Yes,' Richard agreed a bit sheepishly.

'And no need for a messy divorce?'

Assuming it was a joke, Richard laughed and fervently agreed.

Kenda, who was beginning to know Carrick better, stared intently at his grim face and even grimmer mouth. 'I misjudged him,' she said quietly. 'I thought he was cheating.'

'And now you've discovered he wasn't?'

'Yes. It was a mistake.'

'A mistake his wife knows about?'

'Of course she knows!' Richard plunged in. 'Good heavens, you don't think I'd do anything without her knowledge, do you?'

'Obviously not. I must be old-fashioned.'

'Well, you are if you think it's best to keep things from your wife!'

'Fearsome, is she?' Carrick enquired politely.

'Yes. No. How did the training go? I'm sorry I wasn't here, but you obviously know *why* I wasn't,' he added, with a dark look at Kenda.

'Yes,' he agreed, 'and we managed very well. 'Didn't we, Kenda?'

'Yes,' she admitted absently as she continued to stare at him. 'Which end of the stick are you grasping?' she asked interestedly.

'The end you presented. Are you staying?' he asked Richard.

'If I may.'

'Certainly you may. I'm sure Kenda will see you settled in. I have to go out, I'm afraid. I'll see you later. Oh, and Kenda, don't forget what I told you about the dog. He doesn't sleep in the bedrooms.

Any of them.' With a little dip of his head he walked off, ran lightly down the staircase towards the kitchen.

'What's the matter with him?' Richard asked in bewilderment. 'I know he can sometimes be aloof, but that was positively freezing! Doesn't he *want* me here? And what was all that about a stick?'

'Nothing,' she said, a rather angry little glitter in her eyes. 'He makes assumptions.'

'About what?'

'Anything! Come on; I'll show you where you can sleep.' Taking him to the room that adjoined hers—deliberately—she showed him inside, remained leaning in the doorway whilst he unpacked. 'I'll pay you back when I get paid,' she told him quietly. 'Or whenever I get whatever advance the publishers are intending to give me.' And then she smiled—a funny, disbelieving little smile. 'Are they *really* going to publish my manuscript?'

He turned, smiled. 'Yes. Really. It was very good.'

'Limited market, though,' she demurred, determined not to get *too* excited.

'Oh, I don't know. If you can get the schools to take it up... They don't like the title, by the way.'

'Why not?' she demanded with an incensed little sniff. 'It's a very good title.'

'For fiction, maybe. *Was There A Dragon?* doesn't exactly conjure up medieval history made easy.'

'Medieval history made *interesting*,' she corrected him. 'I thought it would attract a child's attention.'

'But not a teacher, or a harassed mother looking for an educational Christmas present for her darling.'

'What do *they* want to call it?'

He gave a little snort of laughter. '*Medieval History Made Easy*.'

'That's boring!'

'But intelligible. How have you been getting on with Carrick?'

Passionately? 'All right,' she said quietly. Until the stick gets grasped by the wrong end. 'He thinks...' Abandoning it, deciding it was definitely best not to tell Richard that Carrick thought, judging by his face, that they'd been having a steamy affair and were about to re-embark on that same steamy affair, she remembered that she'd left the publisher's letter in the lounge and walked back to retrieve it. She didn't want *him* to see it, did she? Otherwise, he might reverse the stick!

When she'd put it safely in her room and returned to Richard's, she asked, 'Did they want any other changes?'

'I don't think so.' Turning, a wry smile etching his round face, he congratulated her. 'It was a job *very* well done.'

'Thank you. And I'm sorry about—well, you know. In future, I promise I'll look before I leap.'

'A promise I doubt you'll ever keep. Impulse *swamps* you, doesn't it?'

'Yes.' But she wasn't going to let it swamp her where Carrick was concerned. She was going to be calm, rational, *ask* why he should immediately think she and Richard had been having an affair. Because that was what he thought. His barbed little references couldn't have implied anything else.

She could see it might have looked like that, could see that he might not know anything about the manuscript, could see that to him the wrecking of Richard's possessions might have been the work of a woman scorned in love, but she had *told* him that she'd only had one intimate affair, told him that it was in the past.

It might have looked as though she and Richard were *going* to have an affair, but then, if she'd been involved with Richard, would she have leaped into Carrick's bed as quickly as she had? No, of course she wouldn't. But, having leapt, did he now think she was going to transfer her affections to Richard? Presumably he did.

Don't get cross, she warned herself. Do not, on any account, get cross! Don't wait up for him. Don't rush in with accusations! Sleep on it, and then, in the morning, calmly, rationally, you can discuss it with him.

'I think I'll turn in,' she said quietly. 'I'll see you in the morning. And—thank you.' With a funny little shrug, she gave him a tentative smile. 'I *am* sorry. I don't deserve you for a friend, do I?'

'No,' he agreed, his own smile a denial.

Returning to her room, she quietly closed the door, and when she was undressed and lying in the wide bed—a very cold and empty bed—she picked up the letter, read it again.

She'd had such hopes of the manuscript. The writing of it had helped to keep her sane, calm, for months, and now that it was, unbelievably, *wanted* all she could think about was Carrick. Carrick, who had mistrusted her, made love to her, and who now thought . . .

She didn't know that. Yes, she did. She knew exactly what he had been thinking, and she didn't want to wait until the morning. Kenda was an *immediate* person. She didn't weigh things up, didn't consider the pros and cons, she acted. And nine times out of ten, she was right. Richard had been a tenth time. Peter hadn't, nor James, nor all the other distasteful little episodes she had been involved in.

She thought she would probably hear when Carrick came back from wherever he'd been... And just where *had* he been? Walking off his own temper? Hurt? No, she denied sadly, not hurt; you only got hurt if you cared. Temper and self-vilification... No, she would think about her book, plan the future, wait for him, and then confront him. Talk. And not lose her temper, she promised herself.

An hour later, she heard Murphy begin to howl and sighed. Not *another* night spent in the hall! Perhaps he would stop, settle down ... Waiting, listening, she sighed again when the howling increased in volume. Oh, Murphy, Murphy. Pushing the covers aside, shoving her feet into her slippers, she was just reaching for her robe when the door opened and Richard walked in wearing nothing but pyjama bottoms—with the dog.

'Martin said he's yours!' he accused her.

'Yes.'

'He's been howling outside my door for hours!'

'Minutes,' she corrected him.

'Then if you heard him, why didn't you do anything about it?' he demanded, incensed.

'I was just going to. Oh, Murphy, you are a wretch!' she exclaimed as she took him from Richard. He wagged his tail, looked hopeful.

'And don't look at me like that; you have to sleep in the hall. Carrick said so!'

'Yes,' Carrick agreed coldly from the open doorway. 'He did.' He glanced from Kenda, dressed in a skimpy nightie, to Richard, in crumpled pyjama bottoms, and gave a mirthless smile. 'Your— reunion seems destined to be interrupted, doesn't it?'

'And if you're thinking what I think you're thinking,' Kenda pronounced equally coldly, 'don't. Because you'd be wrong.'

'Would I?'

'Yes.'

'Lack of opportunity?' he derided her.

'No, lack of desire.'

'I don't believe you. And take that dog down to the hall.' Without waiting for an answer, he walked along to his quarters and went inside.

'Oh, I'll do better than that,' she promised grimly.

'What was that all about?' Richard asked in bewilderment.

'Nothing. Go back to bed.'

'Now, Kenda,' he began placatingly, 'I don't pretend to know what's going on, but I know you, and I know that look in your eye, so don't, please, do anything we'll both regret.'

'We?' she asked coldly. 'Oh, there's no *we* about it. Worry not; I shan't involve you! But if I'm not here in the morning don't be at all surprised.'

'Kenda...'

'Can I still use your flat?'

'Kenda!'

Giving him a smile that was totally without humour, she ushered him out. 'Go to bed.'

'No. What are you going to do?'

'Nothing. I'm not going to do anything.'

'Yes, you are, and I refuse to become involved in one of your mad schemes. Carrick isn't like me! *He* won't take retribution lying down!'

'I'm not going to offer him retribution. Go to bed.' With a sudden smile, she kissed him quickly on the cheek, gave him a little push. 'Go to bed. And thank you.'

Throwing up his hands in defeat, he walked slowly along to his room, looked back once, then went inside.

Her smile dying, her face as grim as Carrick's had been, she went back into her room and shut the door. She obviously wasn't even worth an explanation! So be it. Her mouth a tight line, she put Murphy on the floor, dragged on clean underwear, jeans and a thick sweater, and shoved everything else in her case. Picking up the precious letter, she put it on top and firmly closed the lid. Pulling on her boots, she shrugged into her coat, picked up the dog, case and her handbag, and walked out.

After struggling down to the hall, she set her case down whilst she unbolted the heavy door, then, leaving it wide open, she picked up her case and walked across to her car. Shoving everything in, and putting Murphy on the back seat, she strode across to the outer gate—and discovered that it was locked with a key not a bolt, and that the key was nowhere to be seen. Aiming a kick at it, she eyed it malevolently, and then glanced thoughtfully at her car, then back to the gate.

A grim smile playing about her mouth, she returned to the car, climbed in, revved the engine, lined it up with the gate—then gave a startled cry and stalled the engine as the door was snatched open and the keys removed from the ignition.

'Are you *mad*?' Carrick exploded. He sounded out of breath. 'That gate is solid *oak*! Be quiet!' he ordered Murphy, who'd begun barking, and the dog subsided with a hopeful wag of his tail. 'Do you *want* to kill yourself?'

'Richard told you,' she said flatly. 'And don't shout at my dog.'

'I haven't seen Richard,' he denied. 'Move over.'

'No.'

'Move *over*!' He put a foot inside, and she scrambled across the gearstick to the passenger seat and hastily unlatched the door. He threw himself across, slammed it shut again. Half lying across her thighs, hand still on the doorhandle, he quickly snapped down the lock, fended off Murphy's over enthusiastic tongue and stared into her mutinous face. 'You would have killed yourself,' he stated quietly.

'Unlock the gate.'

'No.'

Grabbing his hand, she tried to move it from the doorhandle, glaring at him mutinously when he refused to release it. 'Get off my legs.'

'No.'

'You can't keep me here by force, and whichever way I go, even if I have to scramble over the wall and walk, I *am* going. I won't say it's been a pleasure because I don't think it has. You can keep the rest of my salary in lieu of notice. Or sue me.'

He continued to watch her, his face inscrutable in the darkness, and then asked gently, 'Don't you *ever* confront anyone with an explanation?'

'No.'

'But why?' he demanded, perplexed. 'Why do you always just run?'

'Because no one ever believes me!' she said fiercely. '*You* weren't about to! I could see what you were thinking!'

'You could see *some* of it,' he argued.

'*Some* of it was enough!'

Still watching her thoughtfully, he stated quietly, 'You expect men to betray you, don't you?'

'Why not?' she scoffed. 'They always have. I sometimes think men are afraid of me.'

'I expect they are,' he agreed. Slowly righting himself, still poised to prevent her leaving, he gently pushed the dog back onto the rear seat, instructed him to lie down, and continued, 'Most men don't want astonishingly beautiful girlfriends; it makes them afraid, possessive, jealous, always waiting, suspecting another man's compliments. And you're not only astonishingly beautiful, you're forceful, passionate. You espouse causes.'

'How do you know?' she demanded bitterly. 'You only ever listen to rumour.'

'And are you so hidebound, so angry that you never try to see things from another's viewpoint?'

'Why should I?'

'Because it's fair. Because I'm asking,' he insisted gently. 'You aren't a rational lady.'

'According to you, I'm not a lady at all!'

'Stop putting words in my mouth, and I meant that I am—rational, I mean, not a lady.'

'Don't make jokes; I'm not in the mood.'

He sighed again, held her hand, despite her trying to free it. 'I'm not impulsive, Kenda. I never have been, which is no doubt why the army suited me very well.'

'I can imagine—all ordered and regimented,' she snapped tartly.

'Yes. Everything in its place. Rash behaviour could get you killed, or someone else. I've never met anyone like you.'

'How dull your life must have been!'

'Yes,' he agreed. 'Something was always missing, only I didn't know what it was. I was so restless— until I met you. A ton of bricks wasn't in it. Only, because I'd always rationalised everything, fool that I was, I tried to apply the same principles to you. Needless to say, they didn't work. Nearly everyone I met told me to stay clear of you, that you were promiscuous, troublesome; only, sometimes there was such a look of—anguish in your eyes. I tried to rationalise that too. Told myself it was defiance.'

'It probably was. And do you think I cause trouble just for the hell of it? Because I enjoy it? I have a great capacity for love, laughter, happiness, but no one ever wants it. Not one damn person. I start over with such *hope*, dust myself off, start again, and *wham*—all rotten. I knew I shouldn't start an affair with you. I *knew* that.'

'And you think that's all I wanted? An affair?'

'Yes! You said so!'

'I was fighting a battle,' he explained quietly. 'Fighting hormones and need with common sense. I can't remember how many times in the past six months I told myself not to be a fool, to forget you, but you would pop into my mind at the damnedest moments and haunt me. And so, against my better judgement, I tried to find you. Only, no one knew where you were.'

'Richard knew.'

'As I said before, Richard wasn't telling. What *is* it between you two?'

'A steamy affair!'

'No, it isn't. Come on, what is it?'

'You mean you didn't *ask* him?'

'I haven't seen him.'

'Not now!' she returned impatiently. 'In the hotel!'

'I didn't see him there either. So tell me.'

Turning her head, she stared at him, maintained a stony silence.

'*Tell* me!'

With a little shrug, she stated flatly. 'A book.'

'A *book*?' he exclaimed incredulously.

'Yes.'

'Well, go on!'

'Why? So you can mock that too?'

'Kenda!' he said warningly. 'Just tell me.'

With another shrug, she said dismissively, 'I wrote one.'

'*And?* Do I have to drag it out of you word by word?'

'No! All you have to do is go away and leave me alone! You *believed* I was—' She bit the sentence off unfinished, then said with quiet dignity, 'I wrote a medieval history for children. I was given no reference when I left the museum, and, because jobs for historians are few and far between, even if you do have references, I decided to do something that had been in my mind for ages. I had the time,' she said a trifle bitterly, 'if not the funds. I still had some of my salary left and, if I didn't have to pay

rent, I thought I could manage for a while.
Richard's been a friend for ages, and he let me use
a flat he owns.'

'And then?'

'I finished it, asked Richard what he thought.
He said it was fine, that he knew someone who
might publish it, but it might take a few months.
I tried to find a job, temporary work—money was
getting tight—and after weeks of fruitless searching,
living off Richard, he asked if I'd consider coming
here. He said he would come down with me, introduce us, but he wanted to spend the weekend at
the hotel first. In separate rooms,' she emphasised.

'But why a hotel? If you weren't—'

'We weren't!' she denied fiercely. 'It was to be a
celebration. Only, I didn't know that. It puzzled
me, but I didn't object. I'd known Richard for
years, knew he was happily married, knew and
loved his wife—so I agreed.'

Taking a deep, painful breath, she continued,
'And then, whilst Richard was out checking golf
courses, a courier came with a letter. It was from
the publishers—the publishers Richard had given
my manuscript to. It wasn't sealed, only with one
of those clip things, so I opened it. And no,' she
insisted with hasty defiance, 'I do not normally go
around opening other people's letters!'

'I didn't say a word,' he said mildly.

'You didn't have to! And I only opened it because it had the publishers' name on the envelope—the publishers I knew Richard had given
my manuscript to! And inside,' she resumed quietly,
'I found formal acceptance of my book. *My* book,
but with Richard's name as the author. He'd been

secretive, evasive every time I'd asked him about
it—'

'And so you jumped to conclusions?'

'Yes, to my shame. I thought he'd stolen it, was
having it published under his own name.'

'And instead of asking him you shredded his
clothes.'

'And the letter, yes,' she agreed, still defiant.

'I should count myself lucky, shouldn't I,' he
asked ruefully, 'that all I was about to get was a
rammed gate? Shouldn't I?' he persisted when she
averted her face. 'You could have caused untold
havoc in the storerooms, the armoury. Why didn't
you?'

'Richard and I weren't having an affair,' she said
stonily.

'And that's the difference?'

'No, I was just telling you. I am so *tired* of all
this! Of never being able to have a relationship, of
suspicions and explanations, of *trying*! Unlock the
gate, Carrick.'

'No. Were you *really* intending to ram it?'

'Yes.'

'You could have killed yourself.'

She shrugged.

'Don't you care?'

'Not when I'm in a temper, no.'

Staring at her averted face, still smoothing the
fingers he held, he said quietly, 'That day you found
the puppy—'

'Yesterday,' she put in shortly.

'Yesterday? Dear Lord, it feels like a year. You
wondered why I was angry.'

'You told me why you were angry.'

'No, I didn't. When I was coming to look for you, I saw Richard driving along the top road. I thought you'd been meeting him behind my back.'

Jerking her head round, she stared at him. 'You said . . .'

'I know what I said.'

'A lie?'

'An excuse. The womanising neighbour does exist, but apart from being sick with worry at your long absence from the castle I was—frightened.'

'Foul.'

'Yes.'

'And you thought that I was so lacking in morals that I would leap from your bed to Richard's without a qualm.'

'No! No,' he added less forcefully. 'I didn't rationalise it, Kenda. Just—reacted. Jealousy is an ugly emotion, and not one I'm used to. I've been fighting my feelings ever since I first saw you, and every time there was a chance to get close something would come between us. Peter, my mother dying, Richard . . . And you weren't my ideal. You were never what I thought I wanted. I'd always imagined, if I fell in love, it would be with someone gentle and sweet—'

'Biddable!'

'No, not biddable, but certainly someone *calm*—' he added, with a quirk of humour which was wasted.

'And Lydia was someone to make you forget me, was she?' she broke in tartly.

'Lydia?' he asked in surprise. 'No. I never slept with her, if that's what you're asking. There was no affair. Lydia fancied living in a castle, I think.'

'Lydia,' she bit out, 'fancied *you*!'

'And that bothers you?' he asked carefully.

'No.'

He gave an odd smile. 'I'm sorry, Kenda. I am so desperately sorry—but so extraordinarily glad I always lock this gate.' After a small hesitation, he asked quietly, 'That very first time we met, you felt as I did, didn't you?'

'I don't know,' she replied disagreeably. 'I don't know how you felt.'

'Yes, you do. I didn't try to hide it. Don't shut me out, Kenda. *Talk* to me.'

Staring through the windscreen, his hand warm on hers, she felt her eyes fill with tears, felt them fall, slide relentlessly down her cheeks to drip off her chin, until with a groan Carrick released her hand and pulled her into his arms, rested his head on hers.

'Oh, Kenda, what am I going to do with you?'

'Let me go.' She sniffed. 'I can't cope with this. I need more. I need honesty, love ... I need all the things you can't give. How can people have affairs?' she wailed. 'They make me feel like dying.'

'And me,' he agreed. 'When we went out to dinner, you asked me why I was withdrawn, and I made some excuse, but really it was because it was so unsatisfactory. I thought in my naïvety that alleviating my needs would be enough. That making love to you would be enough. And it wasn't. But a commitment? With someone who would turn my life upside down?'

'Then let me go,' she repeated helplessly.

'Never.'

'Never?' she asked sadly. 'How long is never? And even if it's only weeks, what sort of weeks would they be, with you never sure what I've been up to? Never knowing if you can trust me?'

'I do trust you—'

'No, you don't! Look how you behaved just seeing me give Richard a hug. Look how you acted at seeing him in my room.'

'I overreacted. I was *jealous* Kenda!'

'Jealous?' she scoffed. 'And even if it were true, that doesn't excuse it! You *assumed*!'

'No, I didn't.'

'Yes, you did!'

He gave an odd smile, tried again. 'Martin came to get me. Said Richard had arrived and that you looked set to kill him. And when I hurried along to save him from his fate you were in each other's arms.'

'I was apologising!'

'I didn't know that, did I?'

'I prompted you! I asked you which end of the stick you were grasping.'

'I'm not very quick on the uptake,' he said meekly.

'Yes, you are! You *assumed*.'

'I couldn't bear to see you in anyone else's arms.'

'You *mistrust* me!'

'I adore you. And life would never be boring, would it? That at least is true. You don't bore me. A lot of people do.'

'You can't base a relationship on not being bored!'

He smiled, pressed a kiss to her hair. 'You've been here a week and now I can't imagine life without you. Neither can Martin.'

'I'm not in love with Mar—' Clamping her lips tight together, she turned her face away.

The silence seemed to stretch for ever, and Kenda determined that she wasn't going to be the one to break it. 'Well, go on, say it!' she urged, unable to keep silent any longer. 'You don't want my love!'

'But I do,' he said softly, his voice deeper, husky. 'I was just savouring the thought of it. The feel of it. To be loved by you would be something special. The intensity you bring to everything, the passion— oh, yes, something so very special.'

Easing herself free, she stared at him. Barely able to see his face in the darkness, she snapped on the map light. He squinted in the sudden brightness, but didn't look away from her scrutiny.

'*Do* you love me, Kenda?' he asked throatily.

And with the defiance that was always in her eyes when she was being asked something that might bring her ridicule or mockery she said flatly, 'Yes. You're the *only* man I have ever loved, ever wanted to love. The only man who has ever made me feel like this.'

'And it hurts, doesn't it?'

'Yes.'

'So much,' he said softly. 'Here,' he continued, placing one hand on his heart. 'And here.' Transferring his hand to his throat, he added, 'A *real* pain, as though it's permanently blocked.'

'Yes.'

His movements slow, he reached out, brushed away her tears with his thumb, allowed his fingers to linger on her jaw, then curved his hand round her neck and drew her gently towards him until their lips brushed. It was the softest of touches that brought electricity tingling between them, made eyelids heavy, limbs languid.

His other hand lifted to cup her face, his fingers a delight as they moved on her scalp. Slow and easy, eyes closed, breathing beginning to labour, she allowed him to explore her lips gently, and a little groan escaped her, a hiccuping sigh, as tears moistened her eyes again, wet her lashes until they spilled over for them both to taste.

'Marry me,' he ordered softly.

'I'm not your ideal.'

'No, just someone I don't think I can live without.'

'I don't like the country.'

'Then we'll move to London.'

Stiffening, pushing him away, she stared at him. 'No.'

'No?'

There was the thud of shoes on cobbles, and they both turned in surprise as the driver's door was wrenched open. Both Martin and Richard looked a bit sheepish when they saw Carrick in the car.

'I couldn't sleep,' Richard mumbled. 'Kept wondering what you were up to. Roused Martin . . .'

Glancing at Martin, Carrick gave a slow smile. 'Did you really think me such a fool as to let her go?' he asked softly.

Martin smiled, shook his head. 'No, but if you won't marry her I intend to.'

'She's not in love with you.' Glancing at Kenda, he smiled into her eyes. 'Go away,' he ordered without looking at them. 'And take the dog with you.'

Opening the back door, Martin scooped up the dog, handed him to Richard. 'It's your turn to babysit,' he instructed him drily. 'Come along; I don't think we're needed.'

Still smiling, Carrick reached across her, pulled the lever to lower her seat-back, and settled her comfortably on the horizontal. Leaning over her, he queried, 'No?'

'You like it here.'

'Yes.'

'Marry me?'

'Yes.'

'You want a baby.'

'Yes.' And his voice changed, became softer, husky, as he continued to stare into her wide eyes, and that low spiral of pain began again in her tummy.

'When you mentioned Oliver's son, you looked . . .'

'Yearning?'

'Yes,' she whispered.

'You don't want babies?'

'Yes,' she managed as the pain intensified.

'My babies?'

'Yes.' Her voice a strangled croak, she nodded.

'I love you,' he said quietly.

'You didn't love me earlier,' she protested sadly. 'You didn't love me when Oliver was here, when I brought back the puppy.'

Settling himself more comfortably, tangling one curl round his finger, Carrick said softly, thoughtfully, 'I didn't *know* I did. I refused to think about loving, about the future, but when I walked along to your room, found it empty, found your things gone—then I knew. I felt—frantic, frightened, so—numb, and I knew then that I couldn't let you go. Ever. Who would there be to argue with? Laugh with? Love? I would have no one to share my bath, my bed, my—life.

'When my father died, my mother was lost, like a little ghost, and I knew—*knew* Kenda—that was how I would be. To lose something that's so precious is—gutting. I felt sick as I flew down those stairs, felt terror when I saw your car lined up at the gates, and that short distance across the cobbles between door and car felt like wading through treacle. Don't ever do that again,' he pleaded, his voice thick, husky. 'Don't put your life at risk for me. Dear God, Kenda, I'm not worth that.'

'I don't think,' she whispered, 'when I'm hurting. And, however absurd it sounds, I think I fell in love with you the first time I saw you. I wanted you, all of you, for me. But I never get what I want, and so I took what was offered and prayed I could cope when it ended. I prayed so *hard*, Carrick, but when you saw me with Richard, and I—' Breaking off, she gave a little frown. 'Why did he take so long?'

'Who?' he queried, nonplussed.

'Richard. You said you saw him earlier. Why did it take him so long to reach the castle?'

Staring at her, he exclaimed on a little grunt of laughter, 'Well, *I* don't know, do I? Perhaps it took him that long to pluck up courage!'

Her frown still in place, she continued to think about it until he gave her a little shake.

'Never mind Richard; tell me about the praying.'

'Praying?'

'Yes! Praying! You said you prayed you could cope!'

'Oh, yes; I promised myself I wouldn't get cross, that I would be rational, talk to you . . . But I knew I couldn't,' she said sadly. 'Knew I couldn't stand there whilst you told me to go. I *couldn't* have done that.'

'And so you ran.'

'Yes.'

'And I stood in my lounge fighting demons, strode along to your room to ask what on earth was going on—and found you gone.'

'You don't have to say you love me...' With a tired smile, she whispered tearfully, 'That sounds like a cue for a song. But if I could stay for a little while...'

'Don't beg!' he ordered gruffly. 'Dear God, don't beg! I love you! I love you,' he added softly, 'and I would very much like,' he went on wryly, 'to actually find you in my bed when I wake. Murphy will *have* to learn to sleep alone.'

'You came down and covered me up.'

'Mmm. Stood over you with a foolish smile on my face. Kissed you goodnight.'

'Did you?'

'Mmm. I even spoke quite kindly to Murphy. Ruffled his ears.'

'Did you?'

'Mmm. "Greater love hath no man..." Marry me.'

'When you're sure.'

'I am sure.'

'When you're positive, then.'

'I am positive. If you don't marry me you'll have to marry Martin...'

'I like Martin.'

'But you don't love him.'

'No.'

'But you love me.'

'Yes.'

He smiled, gathered her closer, whispered, 'And what would you say if I said I didn't believe you?'

'*What?*'

'See? Marry me.'

'All right. If it doesn't work out,' she asked shakily, 'do I get to keep Martin?'

'We'll share him. You can have him weekends and holidays.'

With a tiny smile, a little sob, she wound her arms round his neck, buried her face in his throat. 'I'll try to change,' she promised.

'I don't want you to change. And I can't reach your mouth.'

Raising it obediently, eyes still closed, she gave herself up to a kiss that scorched, then she moved to accommodate caressing fingers that burned, and cried aloud in pleasure and shock as they slid beneath her sweater, touched her breast, moved to the waistband of her jeans. Restless fingers, warm and impatient.

'Wouldn't we be more comfortable in bed?' she gasped.

'No. I like adventures.'

'You said that to Martin,' she remembered unsteadily.

'Yes.'

'This could be a big one.'

He smiled. 'I intend it to be.'

MILLS & BOON®

Next Month's Romances

$\heartsuit$

Each month you can choose from a wide variety of romance novels from Mills & Boon. Below are the new titles to look out for next month from the Presents and Enchanted series.

Presents™

Enchanted™

FREE!

FOUR FREE
specially selected
Enchanted™ novels
PLUS a FREE Mystery Gift
when you return this page...

Return this coupon and we'll send you 4 Mills & Boon® Enchanted™ novels and a mystery gift absolutely FREE! We'll even pay the postage and packing for you.

We're making you this offer to introduce you to the benefits of the Reader Service™– FREE home delivery of brand-new Mills & Boon Enchanted novels, at least a month before they are available in the shops, FREE gifts and a monthly Newsletter packed with information, competitions, author profiles and lots more...

Accepting these FREE books and gift places you under no obligation to buy, you may cancel at any time, even after receiving just your free shipment. Simply complete the coupon below and send it to:

MILLS & BOON READER SERVICE, FREEPOST, CROYDON, SURREY, CR9 3WZ.

READERS IN EIRE PLEASE SEND COUPON TO PO BOX 4546, DUBLIN 24

NO STAMP NEEDED

Yes, please send me 4 free Enchanted novels and a mystery gift. I understand that unless you hear from me, I will receive 6 superb new titles every month for just £2.20* each, postage and packing free. I am under no obligation to purchase any books and I may cancel or suspend my subscription at any time, but the free books and gift will be mine to keep in any case. (I am over 18 years of age)

N7XE

Ms/Mrs/Miss/Mr _____
BLOCK CAPS PLEASE

Address_____

_____

_____ Postcode _____